TAX ON MARRIAGE

VERITY PLEYDELL, wife of a bank manager in a small town in the Home Counties, devotes some of her excessive vitality to writing a desert romance, which proves to be a tremendous best-seller. As a result, she leaps into the public eye, and finds this very pleasant until she discovers that her earnings, on top of her husband's, put him into the super-tax class. Verity is so incensed at this that she insists that they shall be divorced, and much against his will, Brewster, her husband, agrees. Thereupon one unorthodox situation follows another in lively succession. An artist arrives to paint Verity's portrait, and both Verity and her daughter Gillian find him attractive. Iris, the co-respondent in the divorce case, professes a real inclination towards the little bank manager, and turns up at his home. Finally, Verity decides that all this excitement and restlessness does not compensate for the loss of her cosy home and circle of friends, and she is thankful to return to her niche as a small-town matron with a devoted husband.

CHARLES HATTON

Tax On Marriage

JOHN LONG LIMITED

LONDON * NEW YORK * MELBOURNE
SYDNEY * CAPE TOWN

First published 1953

Printed in Great Britain
by The Anchor Press, Ltd.,
Tiptree, Essex

CONTENTS

CHAPTER I

BANKING BUSINESS TRANSACTED

BREWSTER PLEYDELL respectfully ushered out his client from the manager's office and carefully closed the door. Then he returned to his revolving chair at the wide and scrupulously tidy desk. Resting his arms on the elbows of the chair, he experienced the old familiar sense of fulfilment. This was his world.

It was not a room that appealed to the aesthetic senses, but it was solid and reassuring, from the massive leather-topped desk to the ornately framed portrait of Luther Girdlestone, first chairman of the Central Bank Limited in the year of its foundation, 1852.

The Firbright branch of the bank was identical in its essentials with the sixteen hundred and forty-eight other offices of this famous institution, but Pleydell liked to think of it as his own creation, an expression of his personality. After all, he had managed it for twelve years, and liked to boast that he knew every one of his twelve hundred-odd current account customers personally, and that the business had almost doubled since he took over.

Naturally, he was a leading figure in the life of this little town which had grown so rapidly since the fast train service from Baker Street had been started. He was present upon all the major occasions, and treasurer of at least half of the local organizations. And Verity, his wife, was on almost every committee in the town. When it came to organizing any new endeavour, hers was always the first name to be mentioned.

Yes, the Pleydells had quite a niche in the affairs of Firbright, and everybody said the town wouldn't be the same without them. But it was only when he sat in his sanctum that Pleydell felt really supreme—far more so than in any room in the Edwardian red-brick mansion on the outskirts of the town where he lived.

This office was exclusively his domain; he even felt capable of dominating his wife's powerful personality in these familiar surroundings. There was no one who could deny his authority in here, and his word was final. Of course, there were the dictatorial and slightly abrupt voices from Head Office that emerged through the telephone from time to time, but there was always something not quite real about them.

He had to obey their instructions. In point of fact, he could not sanction an overdraft of more than £200 without reference to H.O. All the same, the customers did not know that unless he told them, and he only let out the secret when Head Office were getting particularly insistent about an overdraft and threatening legal proceedings. To the great majority of his clients he was a financial wizard with all-embracing power. Which was a considerable compensation to a man who was a cipher in his home.

Portly, middle-aged Brewster Pleydell was married to a woman of abundant temperament and boundless nervous energy. He often envied Verity her apparently unlimited vitality. Verity frequently awoke at five in the morning, took up the note-book she kept at her bedside and began furiously jotting down notes for a lecture, a recipe she had just re-collected, a menu for dinner or perhaps a few verses of a poem.

Verity was very prone to poetry; she had had a couple of slim volumes published at her own expense by a local firm of printers and had devoted herself to selling them with such energy that, to everybody's surprise, she had disposed of every copy and even showed a small profit. Her husband was not a little relieved, for Verity could never tolerate failure, and on the rare occasions when she had to face it she somehow contrived to make it appear that Brewster was responsible. It was easier not to argue with her, so he meekly accepted the onus.

He dreaded Verity's displays of temperament, which were so liable to lower the dignity of a man in his position. On one occasion when he had been acting as umpire in a tennis tournament and had given a decision against her, she had rushed at him and belaboured him with her racket. Naturally, he had felt bound to resign from the club there and then. Yes, Verity's little bursts of temperament could be quite terrifying.

He often thought they had not been exactly ideal parents to their only daughter, Gillian. They had certainly provided her with all the material things in life, including a good education at an exclusive school, but they had never devoted much time to her. During her younger childhood he had been fighting for promotion in the bank; then she had gone away to school and they saw her only in the holidays, when Verity seemed always to have her own programme planned days ahead so that it permitted very little time for her family.

Sometimes he wished Verity would take a little time to relax. Every minute of her day seemed to be occupied, and if she had half an hour to spare, there always seemed to be a waiting list of jobs to be done. There had been times, too, when this excessive supply of energy had led her into mischief. She had a weakness of espousing minority causes which could prove extremely embarrassing, and she took up several strange cults, one after another. She had a phase for diagnosing all her friends and acquaintances, segregating them into types and informing them how they would react to any given situation.

Then there had been the Yogi business, which had lasted several months and involved performing all sorts of peculiar exercises, most of them on the floor it seemed, which could be very awkward when she refused to stop although there were visitors eyeing her with morbid curiosity.

In fact, she often persisted when visitors were there, and invariably tried to convert them. Worse still, she quite frequently succeeded, for they were usually no match for her overwhelming personality. Verity's proselytes to various cults were to be found all over Firbright and the surrounding country, and they often remained loyal long after she had abandoned the craze herself.

Brewster Pleydell stared thoughtfully into the fire set in its red mahogany mantelpiece and reflected that he really should have married a less exciting woman, one of the hunting families from the surrounding neighbourhood; perhaps a girl who would have devoted her life to him and at the same time brought some useful connections.

Verity had certainly been a beauty in her day, and half the young men in the town had danced attendance upon her during the three years before she had finally settled on Brewster Pleydell. He was only twenty-four when they married, and indeed they could not have done so but for the fact that he suddenly received a legacy from a second cousin which brought him in an income of ten pounds a week. When they heard of this, the bank authorities gave the young couple their blessing.

It all seemed a very long time ago; he was forty-eight now and practically bald. Nor was there any mistaking his tendency to middle-aged spread. On the other hand, Verity, who was forty-five, looked no more than thirty, although she used comparatively little make-up. She had always insisted that this was because she kept herself mentally young and alert, and had never allowed her mind to get into a groove.

It mystified her husband; there was something slightly uncanny about it. Her face always had a positively healthy glow as if it were preserved by some mysterious rejuvenating fluid. It was a fairly plump face and showed very few lines. In fact, there were times when Gillian looked considerably more haggard than her mother.

He sometimes worried what he would do about Verity. She seemed to gain more and more energy with the advancing years, and he was hard put to at times to suggest suitable outlets for it. If there were no outlets, she was liable to discharge herself like a coiled spring and upset his domestic peace. Like the time when she had the idea of everybody walking around barefooted in the house to strengthen the muscles of the feet. That phase had at least revealed that there were a surprising number of sharp objects lying around even when the carpets had been vacuumed.

Brewster Pleydell sighed and brought himself back to the present with a jerk. There were two memos on his desk, and he scanned them carefully. They explained very courteously to Head Office that the accounts in question would be 'reduced' within the next month. He had been dictating such memos word for word for twelve years, but Head Office seemed to accept them quite placidly—unless of course, the overdraft was not reduced!

He initialled them and placed them in his 'out' tray, then signed several letters very scrupulously: *A. Brewster Pleydell*. The initial stood for Andrew, a name he rather despised, though his wife sometimes used it.

But A. Brewster Pleydell seemed to him on the whole a sound, solid sort of name that might well appear on a list of directors. It had a substantial look, redolent of £20,000 a year and a couple of country houses.

Right from his days as a junior he had always signed 'A. Brewster Pleydell', and had almost come to regard it as a double-barrelled name; they were fairly common in the hunting shires. But 'A. B. Pleydell' was obviously quite out of the question—much too reminiscent of a lowly deckhand.

Pleydell signed the last letter with a flourish and a certain sense of satisfaction. It was to a local M.F.H., informing him that his Hunt Account was £98 overdrawn without security, and asking him to deposit a credit to cover. Pleydell secretly disliked the hunting crowd, partly because his own efforts at riding had never been very successful, and partly because he knew most of them classed him with the tradesmen.

He glanced at the clock on the mantelpiece and saw it was five minutes to three. In a few minutes the porter would slam the heavy front door, the clerks would light cigarettes and prepare to balance their books, and the atmosphere of the bank would become rather more easygoing and friendly. He felt the cardboard packet in his pocket to make sure there were enough cigarettes to last him until tea-time.

At that moment the connecting door between his room and the inner office opened to admit his cashier, Wilmott, looking a trifle worried. He held a cheque in his hand, which he showed to Pleydell, "I'm sorry to trouble you, sir," he began apologetically.

"Yes, Wilmott, what is it?"

"Your wife, sir . . . she's asked me to cash this. It's rather a large amount, sir, and it's crossed."

Pleydell took the cheque and examined it with a puzzled air. Verity had mentioned no cheque to him at lunch-time. It was for a hundred pounds, payable to Mrs. Verity Pleydell, and drawn on a bank in Chancery Lane, London, by a firm called Myles and Paskin. The names meant nothing to Pleydell. What on earth was Verity up to now? "Ask Mrs. Pleydell to come in," he said to Wilmott, who looked somewhat relieved and went out to deliver the message.

Pleydell laid the cheque on his desk and rubbed his chin thoughtfully. He heard Verity's high heels clicking briskly on the tiled floor, and rose to meet her.

She came tripping lightly into the office; she was only five feet two, reasonably slim and stylishly dressed. "Hello, darling," she smiled. "I didn't want to bother you with this. Surely they can give me the money. I want to go to town tomorrow and get a new fur coat."

Pleydell stood with his back to the fire and examined her cautiously for any sign of some new activity. "You didn't tell me about this cheque," he began with some deliberation.

"No, darling," she replied in the tone one uses to pacify a querulous child, "I thought you'd be busy, and Wilmott has always cashed cheques for me before."

"This happens to be crossed. . . . It's drawn on another bank, and we know nothing about—er, Myles and Paskin."

Her eyes opened a trifle wider. "But of course you've heard of Myles and Paskin, darling. They are publishers. . . . A very old established firm. They've paid me a hundred pounds advance on my book."

"Your book?" he queried.

"Yes, darling," she replied brightly. "It was to have been a secret for a little longer, but I suppose I'll have to tell you now after all."

"You mean . . . you've written a book?"

"That's right, darling. A novel. It will be published tomorrow."

CHAPTER II

AFTER BANK HOURS

ERIKA was another of Verity's bright ideas. As soon as Holland was liberated, Verity had seized the first opportunity to take a trip over there. She returned with Erika, who had corn-coloured hair, violet eyes, generous mouth and a manner that Pleydell considered just a little too friendly when there were men about. But it could not be denied that she was young, strong and a very capable domestic help.

She had most of the free and easy ideas of the post-war generation in Europe, and had no intention of staying in any job a day longer than it suited her. However, she had taken a fancy to Verity, who treated her well, and her duties were not particularly arduous. Moreover, there were quite a number of friendly young men and a certain amount of social life in Firbright, where a young and attractive girl was sure of any number of partners at the less expensive dances. Taken all round, Erika decided that England was quite a pleasant place. She was a little tired of the sight of tulips, anyhow.

On the evening of the day Verity visited the bank, Erika was laying the table for dinner when the telephone rang. To begin with, she had been very scared of the telephone when her English had been none too good. Now, however, she was rather more sure of herself, and besides it might be that nice boy from the agricultural camp who had 'phoned her once or twice lately. She lifted the receiver.

There was a crackle and a strange voice spoke: "Firbright 224? Can I speak to Miss Nightingale . . . Nina Nightingale?"

" 'Allo! I do not understand," replied the bewildered Erika. "There is nobody that name 'ere . . . here."

"Well, who'm I speaking to?" persisted the voice.

"This is Mr. Pleydell's house. There is no one named Nightingale."

At that moment Gillian Pleydell came in. She was wearing a copper-red semi-evening frock which suited her colouring, and looking more sure of herself than usual. Observing Erika's confusion, she went across and took over the telephone. She, too, was puzzled, and could only inform the caller—apparently a reporter of the *Daily Comet*—that there was no Nightingale in the house. The reporter seemed reluctant to ring off, however, until Gillian said in a firm tone: "My father is a bank manager and my mother . . . well, she's Mrs. Pleydell, and there's me, Gillian Pleydell. . . . Who? The lady with the foreign accent? That's Erika Verel, our Dutch maid. And that's all. Positively no Nightingale." She slammed down the receiver murmuring to herself, "What's he think this is . . . Berkeley Square?"

Now Erika was looking puzzled again and Gillian had to explain the allusion to her. Erika always got worried if she thought people were enjoying private colloquial jokes. When she was satisfied, she went back to laying the table, and Gillian curled up on the settee with a woman's magazine.

The Pleydells had an alcove in the lounge which was adapted into a temporary dining annexe. This enabled Verity to use what should have been the dining-room as her study.

Gillian looked up from her magazine and asked: "Mother hasn't said anything to you about a Miss Nightingale, has she, Erika?"

The maid shook her head.

"I thought perhaps she might have been coming to dinner and told people they could 'phone her here."

"There is no one extra for dinner," replied Erika.

Gillian frowned thoughtfully and lit a cigarette. "It might be somebody to do with the Literary Circle . . . or the Inner Wheel. It might even be the Spiritualist Group she's started playing around with. She's probably some dumpy Lancashire medium who calls everybody 'luv'."

"Please?" queried Erika, pricking up her ears.

Gillian waved her cigarette. "It's just a silly expression, Erika. I can't explain it now."

"There is so much of the English I will never understand," sighed Erika.

"You're getting along fine," Gillian reassured her.

Erika paused in her work. "Soon I will have been here six months," she announced. "When I get back, they will pay me an extra fifteen crowns a week at any office if I speak good English."

"You speak perfect English . . . and you have lots of nice boy friends. What more d'you want?" asked Gillian.

Erika made a deprecatory gesture. "I had two—three proposals of marriage when I was in Amsterdam," she assured Gillian.

"In that case, I think I'll come back with you," smiled Gillian. "It sounds far more exciting than this dull hole."

"But there are always young men calling for you."

"Drips, I call them," said Gillian inelegantly.

The telephone rang again and Gillian lazily reached for the receiver. This time it was the *Daily Mercury* inquiring about Miss Nina Nightingale. The conversation was short and sharp, and the receiver slammed down exactly fifteen seconds later.

"I wish this Nightingale woman would turn up if she's coming," muttered Gillian.

"You think it is perhaps a corpse in the closet?" suggested Erika hopefully.

"You mean skeleton in the cupboard," Gillian corrected her, and instantly regretted doing so. It took her almost five minutes to explain about the skeleton in the cupboard. "We're much too respectable for that," she added wistfully. "Bank managers have to be, you know."

"I think that is very nice," decided Erika, putting the finishing touches to the table. "You are very lucky to have a bank manager for a father. You do not need to go to work; you can stay at home and read books and play tennis and meet nice men."

"I'd give everything to get out of Firbright and take a flat in town," said Gillian.

"Then why not do it?"

"Because they won't let me."

"Then do as I did. Run away with a man. Peter and I lived in one room in Schuttersweg. It was very cosy in the winter."

"Erika, you're making it up!"

"It is true, Miss Gillian. Everything was wonderful until his wife found us. Then there was trouble; that was why I came to England. So you see you can always do as you please—if you wish it sufficiently."

Gillian stubbed out her cigarette. "I don't think I'd mention it to anyone else . . . about you and Peter, I mean," she advised.

Erika flashed her an understanding glance. "Naturally, your parents might not approve." She nodded. "They are important people here."

"I dare say Daddy would be slightly shocked," smiled Gillian, "I couldn't say about Mother. It would rather depend what mood she was in. If she had been reading Balzac to the Literary Circle, she would probably feel quite broadminded. On the other hand, if she had been lecturing at the Unmarried Mothers' League, she would probably take quite a different view."

This was just a shade too subtle for Erika, but she said: "I will not mention it, of course. In any case, it is all over with Peter. His wife was so stupidly jealous."

"What a shame," said Gillian, trying to keep a straight face.

"I was very upset at the time," continued Erika, "but soon afterwards I met Bernard, who is much nicer than Peter."

Gillian permitted herself a smile. "I can't think why you ever left Amsterdam," she said. "It sounds just like the Garden of Eden to me."

"There are other things in life besides men," shrugged Erika, and for a moment looked as if she really meant it. She

B

was just leaving the room when she paused and said: "Your mother was perhaps a Miss Nightingale before she was married? That telephone call may have been from an old friend who did not know she was married."

She looked quite pleased with her theory, but Gillian shook her head, "Mother was one of the Shropshire Collyers," she replied.

"Shropshire?"

"It's the county where they go in for fox-hunting a good deal," explained Gillian.

"Ah, the English think of nothing but sport," sighed Erika, and went off to look after the dinner. Gillian began reading a story in her magazine, and was half-way through it when the 'phone rang once more. She was lazily moving to answer it when her father came in and picked up the receiver. This time it was the *British Newsreel Gazette*, who wanted to take some pictures of Nina Nightingale.

"I don't know what you're talking about," said Pleydell in complete mystification. "There are no nightingales in these parts. Why don't you try the B.B.C.?" He replaced the receiver. "Somebody's idea of a joke, I suppose," he murmured.

Gillian noticed he looked rather tired. His face was just a trifle drawn and his manner less brisk than usual. "Come and sit down and I'll get you a drink," she said. He settled in an armchair and she poured him a glass of his favourite sherry. "That was the third call for Miss Nightingale," she told him. "Have you any idea who she is?"

"Not a clue," he replied, sipping his sherry appreciatively. "Who was it telephoned before?"

"A couple of newspapers. One of them said they had been given our number by a firm of publishers called Myles and Paskin."

"Myles and Paskin!" he echoed, half rising.

"You know them?"

"Yes," replied Pleydell wearily, "they are your mother's publishers. She has written a book that seems to be causing a bit of a sensation."

"Well!" exclaimed Gillian. "Whatever next?"

"Did you know she was writing a book?"

"I have seen her scribbling in exercise books quite a lot

this last year now I come to think of it. But I always thought they were lectures or something like that.

"Nothing as harmless. It was a whole novel—one hundred thousand words—about sheiks and romance among the Arabs," said Pleydell gloomily. "I can't believe that anybody would be such a damn' fool as to publish it, let alone pay her a hundred pounds."

"As much as that?"

"It seems that's only the first instalment. These publishers have told her they expect to sell thousands of copies."

"Aren't you pleased, Daddy?"

He lighted a cigarette somewhat jerkily and drained his glass of sherry. "That sort of thing isn't done in our circles," he said somewhat plaintively. "We are respectable business people. . . ."

"Quite important people have been known to write books," Gillian pointed out.

"I dare say," he replied impatiently, "but they don't turn out servant girls' romances called *The Passionate Mirage*."

"What are you going to do, then?"

"I don't see that we can do anything," he replied gloomily. "She's signed a contract and accepted an advance payment."

"Well, it won't be so bad if she's written under a pen name," suggested Gillian.

"It's bound to leak out. She never could resist boasting about her achievements. Where is she now, by the way?"

"She said she was going to the bank, then to Little Skelding Women's Institute to tell them how to start a dramatic society."

"Oh well, I suppose they asked for it," said Pleydell glumly.

"They didn't. Mother's gone over to insist on their starting one. She says they are the only Institute for ten miles round without a dramatic society."

"Then they've got one by this time. In fact, they have practically won the next festival if your mother's behind them."

He puffed at his cigarette and wondered for the ten-thousandth time why he had married Verity Collyer. She had been a pretty girl and nobody could deny that she was an attractive woman with an overwhelming personality. Why

hadn't he had the sense to realize it would overwhelm *him*?
Why hadn't he foreseen that her limitless energy would wear
his nerves to rags?

Imagine the effort involved in writing one hundred thousand words about people you had never seen and a land you
had never visited! It was almost frightening to contemplate;
to think that a woman who had shared a roof with him for
twenty years should be capable of such a bizarre accomplishment. Once again, he experienced the alarming sensation that
his wife was really a stranger.

If he had not shackled her to the conventional life of the
wife of a bank manager, he often wondered where she would
have ended. He said as much to Gillian now as he nervously
lighted another cigarette "She might have been a great actress
or a film star, or——"

"Nonsense!" interposed his daughter. "She could never act.
She could never get inside another character deeply enough,
and she much prefers to tell other people how to do it, in any
case."

"Perhaps you're right," sighed Pleydell; "but I often think
she would have made a big name. . . . She might even have
been an explorer, like that woman who lived with those native
tribes."

"She's happier here in Firbright," Gillian assured him. "She
can boss everybody and run all her committees. Out in the
world she'd find a lot more people who would stand up to
her."

He ruminated upon this for a while. It was true that Verity
would have met with more competition in London; but who
was to say she wouldn't rise to the top even there? There was
no doubt about her being artistic. Look at all those poems she
had written, and those songs she composed for the Amateur
Operatic Society, and the water colours that were exhibited at
the art gallery. Yes, she was artistic all right and had the
temperament that went with it.

"I don't know why you don't take a stand against her,"
Gillian was saying. "I have often watched you summoning
up your courage, but she always sweeps you off your feet
before you can even make a protest."

"Yes," he admitted, "she's too big for this house . . . too
big for Firbright I often think. All the same, she can be a good

hostess, and she can run a house. I'm sorry you don't get on
very well with her, but I suppose it's to be expected. Your
temperaments are quite different."

"She's never given me much chance to get on with her,"
replied Gillian. "She stifles me at every turn. You see, she
doesn't like growing middle-aged; she's so used to being the
centre of attraction and hates to think she might get some
competition from her daughter."

"Oh, come; I don't think she's as bad as that," said Pleydell mildly, "it's just her high spirits. You ought to play golf
more; it would stop your brooding on such things."

"You know I hate it."

"So did I at first, but I had to stick it for business reasons.
Even now I often think it's a damn' silly idea, knocking a ball
into a hole with a stick. But it gets you out of doors and blows
away the cobwebs. And you meet a jolly decent crowd of
people. Only yesterday I was introduced at the clubhouse to
the new owner of Beauchamp Manor. He seemed a decent
sort; said he'd be in to see me on business next week."

Gillian eyed him enviously. "You're lucky to have your
business to occupy most of your time and get you out of here,"
she said.

"You go out quite a bit," her father argued.

"Yes, but where? Just to meet the same old gang of rugger
men, and the huntin' and shootin' crowd. Not a new idea
amongst the whole lot of 'em. I want to go further afield and
meet some interesting people."

"Everybody seems to find your mother quite interesting.
Why not talk it over with her?"

Gillian shrugged. "That's about the last thing I'd do. Anybody who talks things over with her gets what they asked for
—a monologue!"

Her father slowly took his gold hunter from his waistcoat
pocket, flipped it open and looked at the time. He was feeling
quite hungry by now, for he never had more than a cup of
tea at the office. "Any idea what time your mother will be
back?" he asked. "I'm afraid dinner will be spoilt if she doesn't
hurry."

"That's impossible," said Gillian cryptically.

Before he could ask what she meant, the telephone rang
again. He was about to rise to answer it when he heard his wife

call from the next room, "That'll be for me, I expect . . . I'll take it."

Pleydell sat back again in his chair and wished he had risked a second glass of sherry. It did not always agree with his digestion, but at least it had a kind of fortifying influence, which he somehow felt he was going to need.

The door opened; Verity came in quickly, still wearing her hat, and flung her handbag on to the table. She lifted the receiver. "Hallo?" she said sweetly. "Yes, this is Nina Nightingale speaking . . ."

CHAPTER III

FEAST OF VITAMINS

A WOMAN'S voice which advertised Roedean in every syllable informed Verity that she was through to the B.B.C. Television Service and asked her to hold on. Presently, a very brisk young man who introduced himself as Pat Gartrell came on the line and invited her to appear in his weekly feature, 'Profile Parade', the following Thursday

Before she could reply, he launched upon a long account of the people who had appeared in this feature, and as a result had received tremendous offers from publishers, impresarios, film magnates and boxing promoters. Mr. Gartrell was obviously sold on the pulling power of 'Profile Parade' and was quite determined that there s ould be no doubt about it in the mind of anyone with whom he entered into conversation.

Pleydell, who had gathered the gist of the conversation, expected to see his wife quite awed by this invitation, but to his surprise she adopted a nonchalant air, pointed to her handbag, which Gillian passed to her, and took out her diary. "I'm busy on Thursday morning," she told her caller, "until just after lunch."

Mr. Gartrell said it would be quite in order if she could contrive to reach Alexandra Palace by three-thirty, and, when she agreed, added rather diffidently that the fee would only be one guinea plus expenses, but that it was, of course, wonderful publicity and that the sales of her book would simply rocket up on Friday. Without committing herself, Verity thanked him politely and rang off.

"So *you're* the mysterious Nina Nightingale," said Gillian, in a tone which had a slight edge to it.

"Well, of course; I should have thought you'd have known that at once," replied Verity nonchalantly. "Have there been any more calls?"

"Lots from newspapers and newsreels."

"Oh dear, I hope you didn't offend them. It's just the publicity we need for the book."

"I wrote down the names on the pad. You can ring them back. . . ." She paused for a moment and looked at her mother curiously as she asked, "Why didn't you tell us about this book before?"

"I've been meaning to," replied Verity, taking off her hat, "but the news came through in the middle of the rehearsals for *San Toy*, and that new lecture course was running at the same time. I had so many things on my mind and thought it better not to say anything until the contract was signed."

"But what is this book all about?"

"Oh, romance in the desert and all that sort of thing," she replied vaguely. "I've often said I could write a book like that . . . and now I have."

"Romance in the desert? But you've never seen a desert," Gillian pointed out.

"I've seen plenty of plays and films about it, the same as most people. It's only a question of using the imagination."

"And whatever made you pick on an awful pen name like Nina Nightingale?"

Verity shrugged, "It seemed to go with that sort of book."

Pleydell moved quietly over to the sideboard and poured himself another glass of sherry. Unfortunately his hand shook a little and Verity heard the clink of the glass.

"I shouldn't drink too much of that, if I were you, Andy," she said quickly. "You know how it upsets your digestion when you have it before dinner." He pretended not to hear, and took a large gulp. Verity was about to protest when Erika came in. She was wearing the neat cap and apron she affected when serving the dinner.

"Ah, there you are, Erika!" said Verity eagerly. "Have all our little surprises turned out nicely?"

"Oh yes, Mrs. Pleydell," nodded Erika eagerly, "I did just as it said in the book you gave me."

"Splendid!" smiled Verity. "This is going to be a very special treat for all of us." She gathered her hat and bag. "I really must tidy up before dinner. You can serve it in five minutes, Erika," she ordered. The Dutch girl nodded conspiratorially and went out. Verity turned to the telephone-pad and read the messages on it.

"Did you have a good meeting?" asked her husband.

"Wonderful! There was a sweet old lady of seventy in the Institute; she's going to be a treasure in that play of Barrie's."

"Then they decided to form a dramatic society?"

"Of course," Verity replied in some surprise. "Wasn't that what I went for?" She put down the pad, having decided to telephone her calls after dinner. When she had gone upstairs, Gillian moved restlessly across to the fire-place.

"Everything Mother touches seems to turn into atomic energy," she murmured with a note of envy.

"She's never written novels before," mused Pleydell. "This is something new. I'm afraid this publicity nonsense may get out of hand; I hope the bank doesn't get to hear of it. The new chairman is very fussy about that sort of thing."

"But you can't stop your wife writing books if she wants to," argued Gillian. "Isn't that supposed to be one of the things we mean by democracy?"

"It doesn't work out that way in the banking business," he assured her.

"Why not?"

"The primary function of the bank is to protect its deposits, and if unpleasant publicity is going to affect them, then there'll be trouble."

"I wouldn't call it unpleasant publicity. I dare say you would get lots of people opening accounts just to see what the husband of the famous Nina Nightingale looks like."

Pleydell shook his head. He was reasonably comfortable in his job; he hadn't had a bad debt for five years, and his staff were capable and easy to manage. If it weren't for these domestic upsets, life would be perfect.

"It might even get you a promotion," Gillian urged.

"Wouldn't it be wonderful if they gave you a branch in London—Chelsea or Hampstead . . ."

"Or Limehouse . . . or Stepney," he smiled.

"Even that would be a change," she pouted. "And we needn't live on the premises; we could take a flat near Regent's Park. I'm sure the bank should be very grateful for a bit of publicity like this."

Pleydell sighed. It was surprising how innocent outsiders were about the inner workings of a bank. "My dear Gillian," he said, "the bank has its own publicity department. I admit it's staffed chiefly by directors' sons from the Universities, but I don't blame them for insisting that all publicity campaigns should be prepared in that office. You see, my dear, the main thing about bank advertising is knowing when not to advertise."

"From what I've seen of their adverts, they could do with some new ideas."

Pleydell smiled indulgently. "They make a profit of two millions a year, so I dare say they are fairly satisfied."

He paused and sniffed. Gillian did the same. There was a peculiar pungent smell drifting in from the kitchen, a smell they did not readily recognize. Pleydell thought it was vaguely reminiscent of fried decayed cabbage leaves, but could not be quite certain. Though he was reasonably sure that it was burning the frying-pan. Gillian looked across at him and was about to say something when Verity returned "There seems to be rather a peculiar smell in here," she said.

"I . . . I think it's something cooking," offered Pleydell.

"Oh dear!" exclaimed Verity. "I hope nothing's gone wrong. Perhaps I should have given Erika a Dutch cookery book."

"She reads English perfectly," maintained Gillian.

"She's been cooking for ages; she's quite capable of——" began Pleydell, when he caught a peculiar gleam in his wife's eye.

"I haven't had an opportunity to tell you before, dear," she said calmly, "but tonight's dinner is quite different. We've turned vegetarian."

"We've what!" he exclaimed in alarm.

"I've been trying to tell you this last half-hour," said Gillian.

"It will be so much better for all of us," remarked Verity placidly. She went over and rang the bell for Erika to bring in the meal.

"You mean we get no more meat?" queried Pleydell incredulously.

"Nor bacon. But we get lots of extra cheese and nuts and all sorts of good things. It will be wonderful for your digestion and good for the blood."

"Yes, but dash it all, Verity," he protested, "we need *some* meat, and the ration's practically nothing as it is."

"Then you won't miss it. This is quite the best time to change over. Ah, here's dinner at last!"

"That's good," said Gillian. "Daddy's ravenous."

"I was hungry when I got in," said Pleydell dubiously. "Somehow I think I've gone past it now."

Erika brought in three covered dishes on a tray and set them on the table. The peculiar odour was stronger than ever now. They gathered round the table. Verity lifted the cover of one dish and recoiled slightly as three slabs of a brownish-grey substance were revealed. Pleydell caught a glimpse of it and said hastily: "I don't think I'm very hungry, really. I think perhaps I'm starting a cold."

Verity steeled herself and began to serve out the contents of the dish. "Come along, Andy. You'll find this very appetizing."

"Er . . . what is it, exactly?" he demanded.

"It's called vegetable goose."

"Ah, goose," nodded Pleydell with some satisfaction. "Of course poultry wouldn't count. . . ."

"*Vegetable* goose," she reminded him. "It's a very old recipe."

"Oh well, as long as it isn't a very old goose!" said Pleydell, with a feeble attempt at making the best of things.

Somewhat cautiously, Verity removed the cover from another dish. "Hominy croquettes!" she announced brightly. "They simply melt in your mouth."

"Are you sure they should be that colour?" inquired Gillian rather anxiously.

"What other colour can you suggest?" replied Verity coldly.

"Something not quite so bilious, perhaps."

Verity ignored her and snatched up a sauce boat. "You must try this lovely lentil sauce. It's a special recipe . . . brings out the flavour of everything."

Pleydell did his best to repress a shudder and accepted the plate that was passed to him.

"Don't wait, dear. Eat it while it's hot," Verity urged.

"No hurry," he replied, nervously picking up his knife and fork with patent hesitation. No wonder he had indigestion. Throughout his married life Verity had been experimenting with some food or other. At one time somebody had converted her to Indian dishes, and his mouth had been regularly burnt up twice a day with highly spiced curries. Then there had been the olive oil phase, when she had been convinced that only by taking half a pint of that revolting fluid in some form or other every day could they ever live to reach middle age. There had been the craze for that dark brown bread that tasted like poultry food, and for the wafers that were so brittle that they made his mouth bleed. In sheer self-defence he had formed the habit of lunching out at the Feathers Hotel, where the food, though never remarkable, was at least recognizable.

Verity had finished serving now and was eyeing him reprovingly. "Get on with it, Andy," she snapped.

"Just wondering whether we should have special tools, chopsticks or something," he ventured somewhat feebly. He hastily scooped up a forkful, hesitated, and sniffed it cautiously.

"Well, really!" exclaimed Verity.

"I'm sorry," he apologized, and quickly swallowed several mouthfuls. Then he laid down his fork and poured himself a glass of water, which he swallowed almost at a gulp. He now felt as if a balloon were rapidly inflating in the pit of his stomach. Noticing that Verity was still watching him curiously, he felt perhaps he should make some explanation. "It's rather spicy, isn't it? Maybe I should wait for it to cool down a little."

"Nonsense!" said his wife, who was apparently eating with enjoyment. "It's quite cool enough; the croquettes are delicious."

"I'm certain she's put tulip bulbs in them, chopped very small," complained Gillian, pulling a wry face.

"You're just imagining things," said her mother acidly. "Even if she had, there's nothing wrong with tulip bulbs.

It's well known that the people in Holland lived on them all through the war."

"Funny, Erika never mentioned it."

They ate in silence for a few seconds, then Pleydell said, "Is there any stuffing that goes with this vegetable goose?"

"It's all there."

"I was afraid of that," he muttered to himself, and took another generous gulp of water.

Verity cheered up when she found that the meal was far more eatable than she had feared. "These croquettes really are extremely tasty," she decided, "and they are packed with vitamins A and C . . . or is it B and D? And the vegetable goose is full of protein. When there was no comment from the other side of the table, she went on, "You know, it's tragic to think we have been eating the wrong food all these years."

"We must be lucky to be alive," responded her husband without much enthusiasm, for he did not greatly care either way. The balloon in his stomach seemed to be enveloping him. He wondered how soon he would get an opportunity to take three or four of his magnesia tablets.

"Only last week," continued Verity, "there was an article in the *Vegetarian Home News* that said over fifty per-cent of deaths were attributable to some form of food poisoning. And all through people eating modern processed foods instead of the fresh products of Nature."

"At least they knew what they were eating," argued Gillian.

"That's just the point . . . they didn't!" snapped Verity.

Pleydell took another gulp of water and said nothing.

"There's a sweet to follow, so don't go away," said Verity when he crumpled up his napkin.

"Another big surprise," murmured Gillian, with a hint of sarcasm.

"Something we would never get if we hadn't turned vegetarian," her mother replied with a reproving glance.

Pleydell tried to conceal the remains of his dinner under his knife and fork and waited for the women to finish theirs.

"Tell us more about this book of yours," he suggested, in an attempt to divert his wife's attention.

"I've told you all there is to know," she said remotely.

"Have they really paid you a hundred pounds for it?" demanded Gillian curiously.

"That's just an advance on royalties. I should get a lot more than that."

"But why are all these people ringing up?"

Verity shrugged. "Oh, I expect that's usual when there's a new book published."

"There isn't all that fuss over the scores of books that come out every week; I'm quite sure of that," insisted Gillian.

"Maybe somebody's taken exception to something in the book; perhaps it's going to be banned," suggested Pleydell, trying to conceal the hopeful tone in his voice.

"What exception could anyone take to a story about the desert?" protested Verity, though she looked vaguely uncomfortable for a moment. "Nearly all the characters are sheiks and slave girls and suchlike."

"Surely there's one white girl?" said Gillian.

"There's always a white girl," snapped the author, "but she isn't even remotely like anyone in real life."

Pleydell sat back in his chair and looked across at his wife. He still couldn't believe her to be capable of half the things she had achieved. There seemed something rather frightening about the fact that the woman with whom he had shared a bedroom for twelve years, had observed all the intimacies of her daily round, should be mixed up in matters of which he knew practically nothing. "I can't think what made you want to write that sort of book," he said at last.

Verity collected the plates and stacked them neatly, then rang the bell. "There's a very simple psychological explanation," she said. "You remember that holiday we planned in Egypt, when the bank made you cancel everything? Then the war came, and after that we could never go. It was during those years that I first got the idea. I sublimated the feeling of frustration by working out the plot of several stories about the desert. As soon as I had the time, I wrote one of them."

"As simple as that," murmured Gillian, as Erika came in beaming with the sweet.

"The vegetable goose was superb, Erika," said Verity, who believed in oiling the wheels of domestic management as far as possible. "You did very well."

"Thank you, Mrs. Pleydell," replied Erika. "In Holland we

often made appetizing dishes like that during the war when food was scarce."

"Did you ever do fried tulip bulbs?" asked Gillian.

"Not very often," replied Erika rather wistfully, "they were a special treat, because we did not often get the fat to fry them."

A familiar odour had floated in through the door which Erika had left open. Pleydell sniffed hungrily. "I could swear I can smell bacon," he declared.

Erika beamed at him, displaying her dazzling white teeth. "I am cooking bacon for my supper," she informed him.

"So you haven't turned vegetarian," he queried with a note of envy.

"It would have meant so much fuss with special cards and forms," put in Verity before Erika could reply.

"I do not mind," the maid assured them. "The English bacon is not as good as ours, but I can eat it."

"Wish I had the chance," muttered her employer.

"That will be all, Erika," interposed Verity, who had been serving the sweet. "You can bring the coffee as soon as it's ready."

Erika withdrew, apparently still enjoying some private joke.

Pleydell examined the strange-looking substance on his plate. It was a dark brown colour and in all his long experience of ceremonial dinners and banquets he had seen nothing quite like it. Gillian tasted hers and said, "It tastes slightly of bananas."

"It's banana fritters!" announced her mother triumphantly.

Pleydell prodded the dark brown mess cautiously. "I'd no idea they were that colour."

"They are dried bananas fried in olive oil," explained Verity. Pleydell felt his stomach turn over. He had thought the olive oil craze ended months ago.

"It's wonderful for the lining of the stomach," said Verity. "You know how much good it did you when we had it last time."

"I think if you don't mind, dear," he said with a pained expression, "I'll leave the sweet. I've got rather a full feeling." He made to push back his chair, but Verity forestalled him.

"I had these specially cooked for you, dear," she insisted,

"The book says they are the finest thing known for neutralizing any alcoholic poisons in the system."

Pleydell picked up his fork and conveyed the smallest possible piece of the fritters to his mouth. It tasted like cotton wool flavoured with rancid fat.

"That bacon does smell good," said Gillian, sniffing enviously.

"The pig is the filthiest animal on the face of the earth. Always remember that," said Verity emphatically.

"Strange it's so tasty when you come to think of it," murmured Pleydell dreamily. "Ah well, back to the fritters."

"They really are delicious," said Verity. "I think I'll help myself to some more."

"They're all yours!" declared Gillian with an expressive gesture. She rose and went over to the settee, where she quickly lighted a cigarette.

"If you're as hungry as all that," said Pleydell to Verity, "have mine, too. I've hardly touched them."

"No, no; you must finish them. They're soothing for your dormant ulcer."

It won't be dormant very long at this rate, he thought to himself, as he made some show of obeying. In another attempt to distract Verity's attention from his plate, he said, "Are you going to telephone those newspaper people after dinner?"

Verity considered this for a few moments. "On second thoughts," she decided at last, "it would probably be better if they came to me."

"You know I can't help thinking there's something fishy about that novel," he told her. "Did the publishers give you any actual figures as to how many they'd sold?"

Verity shook her head.

"And you haven't really told us what the story is about," Gillian reminded her.

"There's nothing very much to it," shrugged Verity. "To start with, there's this white girl, the tourist, very happily married to a bank clerk. Then she has a bit of a tiff with her husband and goes off to see the Sphinx by moonlight. On the way back she is waylaid by a local sheik and his men and taken off to the harem."

"You mean . . . worse than death?" queried Gillian with rising interest. Her father shot her a reproving glance to which she seemed oblivious. "Do go on," she urged, "it sounds quite thrilling."

"Well," said Verity, "the sheik falls in love with her, of course, and comes to respect her. He even follows her back to England."

"That's a new twist," nodded Gillian. "Rather improbable of course. Did he bring his camel with him?"

"Don't be ridiculous!"

"The story rather reminds me of a film I once saw," mused Pleydell.

"I dare say," replied his wife somewhat petulantly. "These tales are all written to a formula. Of course, I took the story a stage further than most writers. I made the sheik marry the girl."

"But you said she was happily married to a bank clerk."

"Oh, I got round that all right," smiled Verity. "Her husband realized she was only infatuated by the sheik, so he sacrificed himself and gave her a divorce, knowing she would come back to him in time."

"I must say it all sounds fairly grim to me," commented Gillian. Before her mother could frame a retort, Erika came in with the coffee.

"Ah, another surprise!" said Verity as they gathered round the small side-table, and she prepared to pour out the coffee.

"Not vegetarian coffee?" queried Pleydell suspiciously.

"Of course! It's made from dandelions. Did you follow the instructions carefully, Erika?"

Erika grinned. "It was quite easy, Mrs. Pleydell. At the end of the war I met many Americans who showed me how to make it."

"And I don't suppose that was all they showed you," murmured Gillian inaudibly.

"But how can anyone possibly make coffee out of dandelions?" Pleydell wanted to know.

"From the roots," his wife informed him. "They are ground and roasted. It's much better for you than ordinary coffee. There's no caffein."

Pleydell looked bewildered. So even coffee was harmful. No doubt tea was on the black list as well. He could see himself taking fewer and fewer meals at home. It was all right during the week, but Sunday was going to seem a very long day, particularly if it was too wet for golf. "Yes, but after all, *dandelions*!" he protested. "Next thing we know, we'll be eating grass sandwiches and drinking nettle beer."

"I know you'll like it when you try it," said Verity firmly, as she passed him the coffee. He noted with some relief that she was using the smaller cups.

"I must say it looks more recognizable than anything else we've had this evening," he conceded. "Smells a bit like coffee, too." He took a careful sip and announced, "Pity it's been burnt."

"No, no, that's the proper flavour," said Verity.

Pleydell gulped down the contents of the cup rather like taking a dose of nauseating medicine and quickly returned it to the tray.

"There now, we've all had a perfectly balanced meal," Verity informed them in a satisfied tone.

"Have we really?" grunted Pleydell, in the polite tone he used when clients were telling him their troubles.

"Just the right amount of vitamins and proteins," she went on. "Six months of this diet and your dormant ulcer will have completely disappeared."

Six months of this and I'll have disappeared with it, thought Pleydell, but said nothing.

Verity poured herself a second cup and said: "By the way, I'll have to go to town to have some special photos taken for the newspapers and magazines. I've had two complimentary sittings offered me already."

"Oh really!" said Pleydell, his interest aroused. "I remember I had a complimentary one when I was appointed manager. I got talking to the photographer; he told me that his firm offered free sittings to all managers, in case one of them absconded . . . then the photo would be worth quite a bit to the newspapers."

"I hardly think that could be the reason in my case," said Verity stiffly.

"No, no; of course not, dear," he added hastily, "you are quite a different type of celebrity. He stroked his stomach as unobtrusively as possible. It felt almost twice its size, and yet he was still hungry. He looked across at the sherry decanter and decided against it.

"Are you going out, Daddy?" asked Gillian, noting his restlessness.

"Well, yes, I thought I might drop in at the club."

"I'm told they do rather good chicken sandwiches there nowadays," she murmured.

"What on earth would he want with chicken sandwiches?" demanded Verity.

"Ridiculous!" nodded Pleydell. "As a matter of fact, I'm hoping to see Lockwood there. He wants to have a chat with me about his overdraft, and he doesn't like to be seen coming in the bank, for some peculiar reason."

"I've yet to meet any friend of yours who didn't want to have a talk about his overdraft," smiled Gillian.

"That's what keeps the business going."

"I really don't know why these people can't come and see you in bank hours," said Verity. "I suppose they think that if they buy you a drink or two, you'll charge them a half per-cent less interest."

"Oh, I don't think they are as naïve as that," replied Pleydell. "In fact, I almost wish they were." He reached for the silver cigarette-box and handed it round.

"That reminds me," said Verity, opening her handbag and taking out a packet of cigarettes, "I got these for you at the health stores." She gave him the packet which was unlike any he had ever seen. "They are for your asthma," she explained.

"I hope to goodness you don't smoke them, Daddy, or the place will need fumigating," said Gillian. "One of the boys at the tennis club tried them not long ago. He said they eased his breathing, but they choked everybody else in the pavilion."

Pleydell smiled and pushed the packet into his pocket. "I'll give everybody due notice before I light one," he said. "Aren't you going out tonight, Gillian?"

She shook her head. "For once in a way, I'm going to stay at home and curl up with a bad book."

Pleydell was just going out when the telephone rang once more and Verity answered it. This time it was her publisher, Bertram Paskin, who informed her that he was working late owing to the rush of orders for her book, and wished to confirm an appointment with a photographer. Once again, Verity's diary was consulted, and there was some hesitation and argument before a date was finally fixed. Apparently Mr. Paskin had begun to talk about the book, for Verity suddenly placed her hand over the mouthpiece and said in a tense whisper, "He says they'll sell 200,000 copies by the end of the month."

"And we have to choose a time like this to turn vegetarian," sighed Andrew Brewster Pleydell.

CHAPTER IV

LADY IN THE LIMELIGHT

WHEN Verity calmly informed Mr. Paskin that she had never been nearer the Egyptian desert than Trouville-sur-mer, he seemed in imminent danger of a seizure. He was a pudgy young man with a high blood pressure and squeaky voice. "My dear Mrs. Pleydell, you mustn't breathe a word of it . . . not a word! Especially to the Press," he insisted. "It would destroy the readers' confidence. They like to think the book has been written from the depth of human experience."

"It's all right," said Verity, "I won't say anything. . . . Though it may be rather difficult when I have to do this television."

"Don't worry about that," he assured her. "I shall insist on seeing a script."

They were sitting in his very luxuriously furnished office, with walls smothered in framed originals of jackets of books which the company had published. It was furnished in an expensive off-white material and the curtains at the window were a rich blue velvet.

Myles and Paskin had laid the foundations of a solid business by publishing cheap romances which did a roaring trade with the small libraries and afterwards in paper covers. On the strength of these, they aunched into other series, such as slim volumes of obscure poetry which cost the firm quite a lot of money but were said to enhance its prestige.

Paskin handled all the 'popular' authors; he had a flair for publicity that would have brought him a fortune in any line of business. He had all the necessary contacts for putting over any venture to the public, and it was entirely through his enterprise that Verity's telephone had been so busy.

As he sat opposite her now, he rubbed his pudgy hands together in satisfaction at his latest coup. "We've never had such an instantaneous hit with a novel," he told Verity. "Right from that first mention by Harald Weske, it's gone like an express train." It was not until later that she discovered that Harald Weske was one of the several reviewers who had slim volumes published by Myles and Paskin.

"You have certainly worked very hard, Mr. Paskin," conceded Verity, who was inclined to be cautiously polite when she found herself on strange territory.

"I've just had the third impression put on the machines," he went on. "Nothing but a world paper shortage can stop it now." He put his head on one side and surveyed her thoughtfully for a few moments without speaking. "The next thing is lots of glamorous photos," he decided. "Recognizable, of course, but a definite film star treatment. Readers like to think authors have based the adventures in their books on their own experiences. When you go to Rolande's you must take several dresses—one or two new ones preferably—and let him take dozens of pictures."

Verity sat there clutching her handbag, and wondering if all this was really happening to her. It would take a bit of getting used to, of course. She was quite accustomed to being in the public eye, but only on a comparatively small scale up till now. Her wings must have time to grow.

"Is all this publicity really necessary?" she asked.

"We'll be able to slacken off a bit in a few weeks, once it's well launched. I'll arrange some personal appearances for you at the book stores. All you have to do is autograph copies, and then there'll be some home interviews and one or two other odds and ends that will help with your next book."

"My next book?"

"Of course. You remember we've an option on your next three. You're working on it, I dare say."

"Why no!" admitted Verity. "I've been rather busy with other things."

"You can't have been doing anything that will pay you as well as a sequel to *The Passionate Mirage*," he assured her.

Verity nodded pensively. She had not thought of this

before. Of course it was only this week that she had had any idea how the book was going to catch on. She had never taken it very seriously; in fact, she had been half ashamed of it and would never have revealed herself as the author if it had not scored this amazing success.

"I regard you as our most promising author," said Paskin encouragingly. "You're going to do big things, Mrs. Pleydell."

Yes, she must accustom herself to being an important person outside her own small-town circle. She would have to mix with all sorts of people now; people with first-rate intelligence. It was perhaps a little frightening, but the prospect was quite exciting on the whole. Verity had never lacked self-confidence, and had so often proved to her own satisfaction that she was capable of talking to anybody, from the Lord Lieutenant of the County down to half-educated tramps whom she so often interrogated when she was in search of information. In fact, her lectures were studded with first-hand conversations she had conducted with all conditions of men. . . .

"A sequel to *The Passionate Mirage* would be your best bet," Paskin was urging. "The public loves a sequel. Invariably, it isn't as good as the first book, but they always buy it just to satisfy their curiosity."

"I'll think about it," she promised.

"That's splendid! I'm sure you're bursting with ideas. Oh, and talking of ideas, there'll be a little surprise for you when you do the television show." He noticed that she looked worried, and added at once: "Now it's nothing unpleasant. And I'll see to the script. Pat Gartrell is an old friend of mine. . . . We published his life story two years ago. It sold just under a thousand copies . . . cost us a fortune, but it was worth it in some ways. We've had most of our authors in his 'Profile Parade' . . . wonderful publicity."

The high-pitched voice was beginning to get on Verity's nerves and she was glad when the interview appeared to be coming to an end. However, just as he was about to see her to the door, Paskin hesitated. "There's a friend of mine in the outside office—Jack Manson, a Press photographer with the *Eagle Agency*. I just happened to mention to him on the 'phone that you were due in today. . . . Now if we could get a nice, intimate picture . . ."

Verity had no alternative but to agree, and in came Jack

Manson, a rather shabby individual. Paskin made a great fuss
of him and posed Verity behind the desk, deciding with very
little ado that she was better taken almost full face 'to get the
real value of the eyes'. . . .

"There we are," he said when a satisfactory pose had been
set. "Now, Mrs. Pleydell, you can be signing a big contract for
your next book. Of course, we know you've already signed it,
but the public will be none the wiser."

Verity noticed that Paskin contrived to edge himself
prominently into the picture, but this did not surprise her
unduly. This live wire for his authors' publicity would hardly
be likely to neglect his own!

The shabby photographer exposed several plates in rather
negligent fashion, assuring them that the pictures would be in
the evening papers. Somewhat furtively, he packed up his
tripod and departed, and Verity prepared to follow him.

"Don't forget the glamorous photos," Paskin reminded her,
as he accompanied her to the door again. "We shall want
lots of them for the glossy weeklies. The full glamour, remember!"

With a coy wave of the hand, he returned to his room, and
Verity slowly walked out into the warm sunshine in Chancery
Lane. She paused in front of a motor showroom at the end of
the Aldwych and gazed thoughtfully for some time at an
impressive Harman-Lascelles saloon that was displayed
there. She had always wanted a car of her own. It was true
that she could have the use of their well-worn saloon whenever
she needed it. Andrew never made any difficulties; in fact, he
left the car at home for her more often than not, feeling that a
walk to and from the office kept his weight down. But there
had been times when she had suddenly wanted the car and
found he had taken it to visit a client in an outlying village.
She could hire one quite easily, of course, but that again
wasn't quite the same.

Noticing her interest, an ex-officer type, who had been
hovering at the back of the salesroom, came forward and
informed her that the car was last year's model and was
priced at £1750—'a real snip'. He went on to dilate on its
technical possibilities, but what really fascinated Verity was
its coachwork in royal blue, her favourite colour. Nervously
twisting the end of his pointed moustache, he asked her if she

would like a trial run. She was about to accept there and then,
and had one foot on the running-board, when she stopped.

"I've just remembered an appointment," she said. "Could
you make it Thursday afternoon instead?"

"Certainly, madam," agreed the salesman, with a polite
inclination of his expensively barbered head. Verity eyed him
shrewdly as he took down a note of the appointment. The
wolfish type, she thought. But she didn't doubt she could keep
him in his place. All the same, it was quite pleasant when men
looked at her like that, even though she was in the early forties
. . . it gave one a warm feeling of importance.

However, she was almost frigidly polite towards the salesman, and two minutes later was walking along the Aldwych
once more. Passing a bookshop a familiar image caught her
eye and she stopped abruptly. In one window there was a huge
pyramid of copies of *The Passionate Mirage*, with its striking
portrait of the sheik against a hazy pearl-tinted background.
Paskin had described it as a good selling jacket, and she had no
reason to doubt him.

Before going to the photographer's she visited a small
beauty salon just off Shaftesbury Avenue where she had an
appointment. There was only time for a shampoo and facial
massage, but she felt considerably more self-assured when she
emerged to face the ordeal at the photographer's an hour
later.

She arrived home soon after eight to find that Gillian
had gone to the pictures with one of her young men, and
Pleydell was sitting rather disconsolately in front of the fire,
nodding over the *Financial Argus*, which he was supposed to
read carefully every day, but rarely more than skimmed.
When she asked if he had dined, he nodded gloomily but did
not offer any details. Presently Erika brought in a large
omelette for Verity, and while she ate it she chatted brightly
about her day in town.

"What's the matter, Andrew?" she demanded. "Haven't
you had a very good day?"

He flung his paper aside rather viciously. "I said this
would be the wrong sort of publicity," he snapped. "All the
locals seem to regard it as some sort of joke . . . just as I
expected."

"They'll soon change their tune," she assured him, "when

they see how the book is selling. Here, take a look at this evening's paper." She gave him a copy of the paper, which contained the picture of her taken earlier in the day. "Nothing very funny about that, is there?" she demanded.

In point of fact, it seemed very businesslike. Verity, wearing her reading glasses, was in the act of signing what looked like a very impressive contract. There was even a portentous look about the pudgy Mr. Paskin. A caption under the picture read, 'Nina Nightingale signs her contract for another desert romance.'

Pleydell glanced at it quickly, then turned to the everominous front page headlines. The international situation seemed quite restful compared with his own domestic affairs nowadays. That revolution in Paraguay, for instance, almost sounded funny when viewed simultaneously with the upset in his own household. Of course, this confounded nature food undoubtedly affected one's outlook on life. You couldn't look at things normally when your inside, bloated to twice its size, was for ever popping and fizzing.

". . . and of course it won't hurt your old car to stand outside until we get a temporary garage for it," Verity was saying as he returned to consciousness with a jerk.

"Why the devil should it stand outside? You know what a job it is to start it on cold mornings. . . ."

"I don't believe you've heard a word I've been saying," she declared severely. "I've explained there won't be room in the garage for both cars."

"Both cars? What are you talking about? There's only one car."

"There'll be two on Thursday," she informed him.

CHAPTER V

SON OF THE SHEIK

VERITY found the car salesman waiting for her at the time she had arranged. He seemed to be rather more correctly dressed than ever in a blue suit with a faint pin stripe, which provided an effective background for his M.C.C. tie. The car started without any trouble and he manœuvred it expertly into the stream of traffic sweeping along the Strand. "Is there anywhere particular you wish to go?" he inquired politely.

"Yes," replied Verity promptly, "Alexandra Palace."

The ex-officer looked thoughtful for a moment. "I don't think there's any racing up there today," he told her.

"I said Alexandra Palace—not Alexandra Park," she replied firmly. "And do you mind hurrying? I have an appointment there for three."

He turned up the Charing Cross Road and headed in the direction of Camden Town, wondering if this woman really meant business or whether she was merely out for a free ride. He could have sworn she looked businesslike.

When they got beyond the worst of the dreary suburbs she asked him to change places, and drove the car with expert ease right up to the park gates. Here she stopped the engine and drew in to the side of the road. "All right, I'll give you a cheque now, shall I?" she offered.

The salesman was quite taken aback. "But there's the papers and so on. . . . They are back at the showroom."

"I'm afraid I can't go back there now," she said. "Couldn't you go and get them? I'll be here all afternoon and most of the evening."

He agreed to this and she took out her cheque-book and wrote out a cheque. Then she restarted the engine and drove carefully up the long winding drive and on to the terrace beneath the enormous mast. He took the car back with him, and Verity mounted the steps into the main entrance hall, where a receptionist, who looked like a hostess in a Madrid night club, summoned a page, who conducted Verity to the studio on the second floor. There she found Mr. Pat Gartrell, thoroughly enjoying what had by now become recognized as his own special weekly performance.

Like the majority of B.B.C. producers, Gartrell had joined the staff because he could not find sufficient employment in the outside entertainment world. He was, in fact, a disappointed impresario who would have liked to whirl through existence presenting a new cabaret, West End musical, ice show or ballet almost every week. He bore a perpetual grudge against the backers of the entertainment world because they

evinced no eagerness to entrust him with their capital. So he
had to make do with the B.B.C.

Gartrell was sitting at a small table exactly in the centre
of the studio, with the various visitors to the programme
ranged around him on chairs and settees. He was a stocky,
fair-haired young man who called everybody 'duckie' or
'dearie' in a somewhat selfconscious way, and always tried to
give the impression that he cared nothing for higher authority.

Life, according to Gartrell, was something of a lark, in
which it was fun to thumb one's nose at the high-ups and play
boyish pranks on the stuffed shirts. In vain, his secretary, a
middle-aged spinster with equine features and greying hair
and a reverence for filing systems, tried to call him to order.
Master Gartrell persisted in his pose of the boy who never grew
up, who must have his little frolic at all costs.

His secretary, Miss Ridley, welcomed Verity, warned her
about avoiding the thick cables which littered the floor, and
conducted her to the producer's table, where Gartrell leapt to
his feet and seized both her hands "Why, Nina Nightingale!"
he exclaimed. "Come right in, my dear . . . Miss Ridley! Give
her a script. Gerald, bring that other chair . . ."

He beamed down at Verity and patted her shoulder. "My
dear," he enthused, "however did you come to write such a
simply *adorable* book?" He did not wait for a reply, but
beckoned to a dark-skinned man who was wearing Eastern
robes and standing by himself a few feet away. "You must
meet Hassim Saroud," went on Gartrell. "You two will have
lots to talk about—because he's the son of a real sheik."

Saroud came and bowed low over Verity's hand. "It is an
honour to meet a lady who understands my people so well,"
he declared gravely.

Verity eyed him suspiciously, but there was no sign of the
slightest quirk on the lean, handsome features.

"He's studying law at London University," Gartrell told
her. "I met him at a party the other night and I knew right
away he was just what we wanted to put a bit of extra colour
into your interview. It was an absolute brainwave; I'm going
to pan from a close-up of the book-jacket on to Hassim. . . .
It'll be terrific!" he added modestly. "And I've got the back-
room boys to write in some perfectly marvellous dialogue
between the two of you. It won't take you ten minutes to learn

it. You can go and sit quietly in my office when we've got everything sorted out here."

He excused himself and went off to round up some more prospective interviewees, leaving Verity wondering exactly what to say to this strange young man beside her. She recalled her publisher's strict injunction that she must on no account give away the fact that she had been no further south than the Côte d'Azur, but it was not going to be easy. However, she managed to stall Saroud off by saying she would rather not discuss her work, and instead asked him questions about his studies and his reactions to London.

Rather to her bewilderment, he seemed to have the idea that he must pay her elaborate compliments. "I thought the lady they asked me to meet would perhaps be an elderly schoolmistress," he told her. "There are so many of them in my country; they come on sea cruises looking for romance. But you . . . you are young and beautiful. You have poise and charm. . . ."

The low but penetrating voice went on and Verity wondered a trifle apprehensively if anyone else could hear him. However, both the studio staff and the rest of the interviewees seemed far too intent upon their own affairs.

"Do you always talk like this to strangers?" Verity asked the young man.

"Certainly not. But the moment I saw you, I knew we were not strangers."

It sounded like a bit of dialogue out of *The Passionate Mirage*, but Verity was grateful to him for distracting her from the bustle of these strange surroundings, which could appear quite terrifying if you started to worry about cameras and microphones, and how one would look on a million small screens. Verity refused to let her mind dwell on it. If this young man could appear nonchalant about the business, then a woman with her experience in facing audiences should not allow herself to get rattled. All the same, it was something of an ordeal, and it was high time she took a look at her script.

She was about to suggest to Saroud that they should retire to a corner and read through the dialogue that had been written for them, when Gartrell reappeared in the centre of the floor and clapped his hands to command attention. "Lovely cups of tea!" he announced. "Break till four-thirty."

Verity and the young Egyptian followed the crowd along the corridor and down the iron staircase into the canteen, where a long queue wound out into the corridor. When they eventually settled themselves, Gartrell presided over an animated little group in one corner. It seemed to Verity that everybody but herself was talking simultaneously, but the strident tones of the producer dominated them all. Verity looked round the table and quietly sipped her tea, surveying her companions in the limelight.

There was a Spanish dancer, supplied by the Arts Council; an aged philatelist who was having trouble with his dentures; a young officer who was there to publicize the activities of his own particular department in the Air Ministry; a lion-tamer with a week-old cub; a singer from a newly opened night club, and a gaunt, long-haired man and wife who specialized in making bronze ornaments.

Verity took a quiet look at her script and found it bristled with inaccuracies. She tried to attract Gartrell's attention, but he only patted her reassuringly on the arm and said:

"Don't worry about that, dearie. We'll make lots of lovely alterations after tea. Try one of those vile cakes—the cream is made from horse fat. . . . You'll love it!"

"How horrible!" exclaimed Verity, feeling thankful she had turned vegetarian. She began to pencil some corrections on her script, and presently there was a call for her over the loudspeaker at the far end of the canteen. A gentleman wished to speak to her in the front hall.

It took her some time to find her way there along the labyrinth of high corridors. At first she had forgotten which floor she was on, and it was some time before she realized she had to climb up from basement to ground level.

The car salesman was waiting for her. He had a long envelope which he handed over, telling her that it contained the licence and all the papers relating to the Harman-Lascelles, which she could now drive away. She glanced through the papers and they seemed to be in order. He showed her where he had left the car and assured her there was more than enough petrol to get her home.

Verity did not return to the canteen but took the lift back to the studio, where the lights were now dimmed. It seemed strangely quiet, and she found a corner behind a piece of scenery where she could sit unobserved and study her script. By the time the rest of the company returned she had made all the alterations she considered necessary and also had a fair idea of the whole interview fixed in her mind. Gartrell had assured her earlier that it was not necessary to be word perfect; indeed, that sometimes gave an impression of stiffness.

Banks of mercury arc lamps up above blazed forth their steely-blue radiance to which standard spotlights on the floor added their amber glow. Cameramen, scene-shifters and electricians began to bustle around. Saroud arrived on the scene with Gartrell and they quickly ran through the amend-ments to the script, which the producer passed without any argument. Indeed, Gartrell was not the argumentative type; there were always so many matters piling up on him that he instinctively took the easiest course that offered.

Verity noticed Saroud's great black eyes upon her admir-ingly. "You are so sure of yourself," he murmured in a low vibrating tone. "Most women are so uncertain——"

"Well, naturally I know more than anyone else about my own life story," she tried to laugh it off. But the dark eyes beneath the white burnous seemed to follow her everywhere. She hoped no one else noticed it, and was relieved to see that they were all much too busy with their own concerns. Indeed, the pace was quickening now, for they were due on the air in two hours' time.

Gartrell retired to the producer's gallery away above the studio, and they began their first complete run-through. As Verity came on about half-way through the programme, she was able to watch the others. Before the run-through, however, they retired to the dressing-rooms, where two garrulous make-up girls in green overalls quickly applied a sun-tan make-up which was quite becoming under the glare of the strong lights.

A gaunt-looking man with horn-rimmed glasses now took charge on the studio floor. He wore headphones on a long lead and was constantly in touch with the producer's gallery. He seemed perpetually worried but was extremely polite to the performers, marshalling them beneath the long boom on which was suspended a microphone, and positioning them accurately in front of one of the three cameras.

Verity experienced a terrifying sensation in the pit of the stomach as the camera rapidly tracked in towards her; its hooded eye had that peculiar hypnotic quality with which she imagined a stoat fascinated a rabbit. She found great difficulty in talking freely or in projecting her personality as forcefully as she was accustomed when lecturing an audience. Indeed, if it had not been for the penetrating drone of Saroud's voice prompting her, she would probably have dried up completely, particularly when there was a boom from the studio speaker half-way through, and Gartrell's voice announced: "Just a minute, dear. I've got a piece of delicious biz for you there. . . ."

The business in question merely concerned the turning of the pages of the book, which did not strike her as very original, though she thought it would be impolite to say so. Gartrell had a lot of ideas like that, none of them very good, but his exuberance made them appear much better than they were.

There was now a lot of drawing of chalkmarks to indicate exactly where people had to stand; with more instructions booming over the loudspeaker and studio staff bustling around, hopping over the cable-strewn floor like agile cats.

They had a couple of runs-through, and at a quarter to eight another break for a few minutes, during which the big outside doors of the studio were slid back and great gusts of cool air came in to replace the overheated atmosphere. At five to eight the doors were closed, the loudspeaker warned everybody to stand by, the make-up girls came round with their powder-puffs for a final inspection, the lights blazed up to full strength, the men in shirt-sleeves looked serious for the first time, as if they expected some emergency to occur at any moment; and for a few seconds everything in the studio was deathly still.

The first performers to appear took their places, the Spanish dancer nervously clicked her castanets, everybody cleared their throats, a gramophone record could be heard playing a tinny march in the distance, and an illuminated red sign flicked on to tell them they were on the air.

The gaunt studio manager pointed a shade too dramatically at the opening speakers, who began chattering in animated fashion. Verity felt a sudden urge to go out and be sick, followed by another to rush into her car and drive madly into the night. She gritted her teeth and told herself not to be a fool, that this was going to sell thousands of copies of her book, and that the Inner Wheel would listen with bated breath as she described the experience. She decided to concentrate upon the studio manager, who was busy marshalling people into their positions, signalling to the control gallery, making signs to the cameramen and occasionally finding time to take a peep at a small monitor screen in one corner which showed the picture that was being transmitted.

Verity suddenly felt her elbow squeezed reassuringly, and turned to see Saroud standing at her side. "You are looking wonderful," he whispered.

"What?" queried Verity, who hadn't quite heard, and thought he might be telling her of some change of plan.

"I said you look wonderful."

Verity shrugged impatiently and concentrated again on the programme, which was slipping along at what seemed an alarming rate. Already the lady from Spain was whirling madly round her prescribed area of the studio, feverishly clicking her castanets and baring her teeth like a cornered leopard. As a critical balletomane, Verity was just deciding that the dancer was covering up certain deficiencies in technique with an excess of noise and some emphasis on various aspects of her figure, when she saw the studio manager beckoning to her. She went over and joined Saroud on the *chaise longue* which a cameraman was busily getting into focus. Another camera was getting a close-up of the jacket of *The Passionate Mirage*. The Spanish dance finished in a whirlwind of simulated passion, and Verity could hear the compère at the far end of the studio announcing the programme's good fortune in persuading the latest best-seller novelist to pay them a visit.

In the palm of her hand Verity gripped a scrap of paper on which was written certain significant sentences; this was a device she often used when she was lecturing. Luckily she did not have to consult it on this occasion. Indeed, it was Saroud who dried up at one juncture. She prompted him almost unobtrusively by twisting one of his lines into her own as he was fumbling for words.

Verity told a million viewers how she had come to write *The Passionate Mirage*, how she had always been fascinated by the mystic East; how she jotted down a few hundred words whenever she had the opportunity as a relief from her household duties, and how she kept it a secret from all her friends and even her own family.

Saroud gravely complimented her upon the uncanny accuracy of her descriptions of life in the desert and asked one or two tentative questions on the subject of a sequel.

It was all over almost as soon as it had begun; the cameras were tracking back, the studio manager was making a wipe-out gesture as a signal to his assistants, and she and Saroud were back at the side of the studio, out of the fierce glare of the lights.

Ten minutes later the programme ended, the illuminated sign went out, the electricians snapped off their huge switches and banks of lights faded. Everybody was standing in groups chattering noisily, and presently Pat Gartrell came rushing down from the gallery to assure everybody they had been magnificent, fervently informing them that it was the best programme in the series. He always said that.

After they had all had a drink at a nearby hostelry, Verity, anxious to show off her new car, asked if she could give anyone a lift. It was not at all convenient for her to return to central London, but the roads would be deserted at this time. Four people accepted and they set off to find the car in the car park adjoining the studios. Verity found Saroud sitting next to her in the front seat; the others took it for granted that he was an old friend of hers.

Gartrell bade them an affectionate farewell, and they set off down the well-lighted drive towards Wood Green. The car ran very smoothly, and Verity handled it as confidently as if she had been driving it for months. Indeed, none of the passengers suspected otherwise. Two of the latter she dropped in Bloomsbury, one at Liverpool Street station, and then found herself alone in the car with Saroud, who had a flat in West Kensington. It was nearly ten o'clock now, and she was anxious to get home, but apparently the young Egyptian took it for granted that she would deliver him to his doorstep. She was none too sure of the way, and he was too busy paying her compliments to direct her, so they went off their route twice.

All the time, he kept up a flow of smooth-tongued adoration that she began to find a trifle monotonous. At first, she tried, as was her wont, to parry his advances with swift repartee, but she tired long before he did. In fact, Hassim Saroud appeared to be under the firm illusion that it was his mission in life to flatter the opposite sex at every possible opportunity, and he brought to it all the skill and polish a West End actor lavishes on his latest part.

Verity had almost relapsed into complete silence when the engine gave a series of ominous knocks and finally sighed to a standstill about a hundred yards from a garage in the Bayswater Road. The mechanic who examined the car immediately diagnosed it as 'big-end trouble', and declared that even if they could start the job right away (which they couldn't), it would take four or five days and cost somewhere in the region of £60. With a glint in her eye, she told him to do the job as quickly as possible.

She had been a fool to buy the car without taking somebody knowledgeable along with her; she realized that now. Though she had thought a showroom in such a prominent position would prove reliable enough.

Saroud was anxious that she should accompany him back to his flat, where he assured her the landlady had a bedroom to spare, but Verity, feeling some reaction to her exciting day, was firm in her refusal and summoned a taxi to take her to the Great Eastern Hotel, where she spent a restless night, for the last train for Firbright had departed at 10.10.

Before retiring she telephoned Andrew. She did not mention the purchase of the car, but simply told him that she had been detained after the programme and had missed the last train.

"What did you think of the programme?" she inquired presently.

"Very interesting," was the guarded reply.

"Was I all right?"

"Oh yes—yes, indeed. You were splendid." But he didn't sound very enthusiastic; in fact it was the sort of voice he used when a client asked for an abnormally large overdraft; friendly, but restrained.

"What did Gillian think of it?" she persisted.

"Oh, she thought you were good, too. So did Erika. You made a great impression on her." He hesitated a moment, then said, "Who was that black fellow you were talking to?"

"You heard the announcement. He is the son of some Egyptian sheik—and he isn't black. Just dark-skinned."

"He looked black."

"Then it must have been the lighting." Slightly annoyed

D

at finding herself explaining Hassim Saroud, she announced that she was going to bed, and replaced the receiver.

As soon as she had done so, she remembered that she had intended to ask Andrew to stop the cheque to the car people. It would have to wait until the morning. Anyhow, it would have only involved a long stream of tiresome questions and answers.

CHAPTER VI

PORTRAIT OF A SUCCESS

IMMEDIATELY after breakfast the next morning, Verity telephoned the car salesroom. Very precisely, she informed the manager that it would be useless to pay in her cheque, as she proposed to stop payment until the car was repaired. He would then receive a cheque for the original amount, less the cost of the repairs.

He assured her quite fervently that it was highly irregular. Keeping her temper, she asked him if he would like to take the car back. And for his further information, gave him the address of the garage where he could go and claim it. Eventually, he agreed to the amended transaction and said that he would not present the cheque.

Verity immediately rang up the bank at Firbright, asked for one of the cashiers, and gave him details of the cheque, telling him that she would call in and sign a 'Stop' form that morning. Then she paid her bill and caught the next train home.

She found a pile of letters, several telephone messages, and a telegram from Saroud asking her to dine with him that evening. She tore it into little pieces, wondering how he had discovered her address. There were several people who could have told him . . . it really didn't matter. . . . He was very handsome, of course; plenty of women would have welcomed the chance to dine with him *tête-à-tête* . . . but she didn't want to get mixed up in anything like that . . . though, of course, he was picturesque in a way. . . .

Her thoughts shuttled to and fro as she screwed the pieces

of the telegram into a little ball and tried to carry on a vague converstion with Erika.

He had talked a lot about Kismet; she had tried once or twice to get him to expound on the subject of mysticism, but he had always come back to Kismet and Love, though he hadn't said anything particularly enlightening. . . . It was just the sort of stuff you would read in *The Passionate Mirage* or any other desert novel. Maybe he thought that was what she wanted to hear. . . . Maybe he had enjoyed a lot of success with other women using the same line of talk . . . it sounded romantic enoug hin that velvety voice of his. Just as well he hadn't been talking to Gillian; she was so impressionable. And Erika would have been round his neck as soon as he looked at her with those smouldering eyes. . . .

With an abrupt gesture she flung the ball of paper into the back of the fire-place, and went on opening letters while she planned the day's meals with Erika. It was surprising the number of long-forgotten acquaintances who seemed anxious to return to her life now she was in the limelight. So many women with whom she had taken tea after one of her lectures, or met on some committee . . . some of them wrote in a faintly patronizing manner as if they were doing her a favour in offering to pick up the threads of their friendship. Others were inclined to grovel, their spinsterish handwriting proclaiming that of course she wouldn't remember them, but they were so glad for her sake that she was a success, that they had known the minute they saw her.

Presently her husband returned to lunch with Gillian, whom he had brought back with him in the car. He had come to an arrangement with Erika that she cooked him an omelette whenever there was some strange new dish on the menu, and Verity had decided that it would be rather futile to argue with him on the matter, so meal-times were becoming rather more amicable.

All the same, he was in none too good a mood. Several of his oldest clients had made a point of dropping in to ask him about Verity and 'the black feller', and for once in a way he felt mildly resentful that she should have taken part in this interlude without even mentioning it to him. Of course, he had to admit that she rarely consulted him about her various enterprises, but when it came to a public exhibition of this sort with a foreigner young enough to be her son, he thought she might have considered his position. The way the fellow had made eyes at her was almost indecent.

He sat there in somewhat gloomy silence, while Gillian chattered away, asking her mother questions about television. Erika, too, chipped in whenever she happened to be in the room. Pleydell waited until she had served the inevitable dandelion coffee before asking, "What's all this fuss about a stopped cheque?"

Verity set down her cup. "So they told you about that?" she said.

"I make it my business to know what goes on in my own office," he replied stiffly. "The Stopped Cheques register is brought in to me just before lunch every day. It seems to me a lucky thing you did stop it; there isn't enough money in your account to meet it by a long way.

"I'll be paying in a thousand this week," she retorted somewhat acidly. "I've arranged for another advance on royalties, so I bought a car."

"What sort is it?" queried Gillian eagerly.

"It's a Harman-Lascelles—last year's model. But it broke down and so I stopped the cheque," explained Verity breathlessly. "I told the people I bought it from they would have to pay for the repairs or take the car back."

Pleydell gazed moodily out of the window. "And do you mind telling me where we are going to put this car?" he inquired.

"In the garage, of course," replied Verity innocently.

"And what's going to become of *my* car?" he demanded abruptly.

"We can get some sort of temporary shed put up for it. Though it wouldn't do it much harm to stand outside—after all, it's ten years old now. We've had the best out of it."

He looked across at Gillian, expecting at least a sympathetic glance from her, but she was far too enwrapt in the idea of an almost new Harman-Lascelles.

"It's about time we had a new car," she nodded. "You can get rid of the old one, Daddy."

"Oh no," said Verity quickly. "We shall need both. I shall have to be going round the country quite a bit; I'll have to run my own car. It'll save a lot of time."

"I thought you were going to stay at home and write another novel," he suggested pointedly.

"Oh, of course; I'll do that as well. But I'll have more lecturing than ever now, and I dare say I'll have to autograph copies at bookshops and all that sort of thing. And there'll be a lot of business in town. If I have a car I won't have to depend on that awful train service."

Pleydell sighed. "It's a lot of money to pay for a car. I never paid more than eight-fifty in my life," he told her.

"Times are different nowadays. You know how difficult it is to get a new car."

"I can only imagine you've paid a black market price," he insisted. "And the car can't be up to much if it breaks down before you've driven it ten miles."

Verity busied herself pouring more coffee and pretended not to hear his last remark. Pleydell buried himself behind his daily paper, but obviously could not concentrate upon it. There was a headline rumouring that the bank rate might go up, which made him recoil. Apart from involving a considerable amount of extra work, such a move would be very unpopular with his customers. And Pleydell liked to feel that he was pleasing the customers.

Meanwhile, Verity was chattering away animatedly to Gillian about the trip to town. She suddenly warmed towards her daughter. Gillian had grown much better-looking these past few months; she was much too good for Harold, her most faithful admirer. She would make a brilliant match. Now that Verity had an entrée to literary and artistic circles, she could introduce Gillian to all sorts of brilliant young men who would bring her out of her shell and help her to get rid of her small-town inferiority complex. Perhaps they could take a nice little two-roomed flat as a *pied à terre* up in town, and do a certain amount of entertaining to establish a circle of friends. It would be so good for the girl. She might even get her presented; the poor child had never really had a chance in Firbright.

Possibly her ample, well-cooked lunch had something to do with it, but Verity felt suddenly magnanimous. Everybody was going to bask in her reflected glory; she would even do something for Andrew, and perhaps when she had her London flat she might entertain one or two of the directors of the bank and persuade them that Andrew was the type of man they needed up at Head Office. He had devoted his life and soul to the bank for over twenty years, and it was time they realized his true worth.

Presently he folded up his paper and moodily announced that it was time he went back to the office. Gillian asked him to give her a lift as far as the tennis club, and ran to change quickly. While Erika cleared away, Verity went back to her desk and dashed off answers to several of her letters, the sort of polite answer that nevertheless made it clearly understood that the recipient was fortunate to get such a prompt reply from a busy and successful lady novelist, and indicated that this must certainly not be taken as a precedent.

In between times, there were several telephone calls from local acquaintances who were anxious to assure her that she had been wonderful on television, and displayed a variety of subtle approaches to the inevitable inquiry about the dark gentleman.

"Such a sensitive, intelligent face," enthused Mrs. Winsmore, who was reputed to make a steady living from her daily efforts at the bridge club, and could be relied on to keep abreast of any hint of scandal. "Did you say you met him in Egypt?"

"I did not," replied Verity, "though I believe he is the son of a very important sheik of one of the most ancient tribes."

"Ah! Then no doubt you will be seeing him again," remarked Mrs. Winsmore placidly. "I always say we have to be broad-minded about these matters."

"About which matters?" queried Verity a trifle acidly.

"Oh, the colour question and all that sort of thing. Of course, I know *you* are quite open-minded, Mrs. Pleydell. You get about so. But some of the Firbright people . . . Well . . ."

"You don't think they will approve of my talking to a coloured gentleman?" asked Verity in the tone of a barrister setting a trap for a witness.

"I don't think they can object to your *talking* to him," replied Mrs. Winsmore hastily, "but you know they have rather a reputation. And some women believe all they read in these cheap romantic novels. Of course, you and I know life isn't really like that, but these poor dears lead such sheltered existences."

"I know I can rely on you to tell them the truth," said

Verity cryptically. "And now I really must get on with some work."

"Ah! Busy with another of your little books?" queried Mrs. Winsmore coyly.

"Yes," replied Verity. "Another of those desert romances." And she rang off before Mrs. Winsmore could launch into further apologies. She had probably made an enemy of the woman, but she didn't care. Somehow she felt she had grown bigger than the bridge club and the tennis club and the Inner Wheel. . . . She was like a dictator who must have room to expand. . . . She could almost sympathize with Hitler.

After dinner that evening, when her husband had gone out for a short stroll in an effort to overcome incipient indigestion, Verity decided that here was the opportunity to have a talk with Gillian about her young man.

"Isn't Harold calling for you tonight?" she asked in a studiously careless tone.

"I hope not," replied Gillian with a tiny shrug. "I've given him a fairly strong hint not to come so often. He bores me."

"You seem quite pleased to let him take you dancing," Verity reminded her.

Gillian nodded with a reminiscent smile. "Well, after all, I can't go by myself," she pointed out, "and I don't dance with him more than twice in an evening."

"He's a nice boy," said Verity, placidly waiting her opportunity. "And I'm sure he's fond of you. Didn't I hear something about his uncle offering him a junior partnership in the estate agency?"

"Oh yes," replied Gillian wearily. "That was fixed some time ago. He's always pestering me to marry him."

"Then you haven't accepted?"

"Should I?"

"Of course not, if you don't love him. After all, you are comparatively young, and there's no need to grab at your first offer."

"Just what I thought," agreed Gillian eagerly, hoping that her mother was going to be sensible and spare her a lecture.

"At the same time, he's quite a handsome young man, and I dare say plenty of girls will be ready to snap him up."

"They're welcome," said Gillian with fine disdain. "I think he's a bit of a weed. His nose is too long."

Verity smiled to herself. She remembered how fussy she'd been about men's looks when she was her daughter's present age. "Have you really got anything against him?" she persisted, anxious to make sure of the exact situation.

"Nothing at all, except I don't react to him. Whatever he did to me, I wouldn't be any more thrilled than a politician kissing a messy baby."

"I seem to remember that I wasn't particularly interested in kissing until I was turned twenty," Verity recalled. "Some girls develop rather slowly in that direction."

Gillian's eyes lit up. "Didn't you really, Mother? I was beginning to wonder if there was something wrong with me . . . I mean several of the boys at the tennis club have kissed me and, well, it doesn't seem to mean anything. It just seems silly. . . ."

Verity patted her hand reassuringly. "Don't worry your head about it. And try not to be too critical of the men. I'm afraid the cinema makes some of you girls set far too high a standard," she said with a sigh. "Just try to take them as they come and don't expect miracles."

"I have tried to listen to their silly chatter about golf and hunting and racing," replied Gillian. "It just isn't my cup of tea."

She's at the difficult age when a girl doesn't know her own mind for two minutes together, thought Verity. And it's impossible to do very much about it; she'll just have to find her own way out of that particular wood. Though it won't hurt her to meet a wider selection of men as long as she doesn't let some charming bounder sweep her off her feet. It's up to me to put a stop to that. . . .

"You were always lucky with men," Gillian was saying. "You've had them fluttering around and running errands, letting you organize them into committees and give them their instructions. I suppose it's some sort of gift, really."

"Any normal man loves doing things for an attractive woman. You should know that by now."

"Then I can't be attractive enough," sighed Gillian. "They never flutter around me like they do with you."

"It's just a question of experience. You'll learn quite soon enough. The main thing is not to be selfconscious."

There was the sound of a car drawing up outside and Gillian peered curiously through the window. "It's one of the station taxis," she announced. "I wonder who it can be."

They heard Erika answer the doorbell, and presently she came in to say that a gentleman wished to see Verity urgently.

"Don't you know who it is?" she asked.

"I have never seen him before, Mrs. Pleydell," the girl replied.

"I expect it's another reporter or photographer," said Gillian.

"Surely not at this time," frowned Verity.

"Didn't he give his name?" asked Gillian.

"He said you would not know it."

"You'd better ask him to come in," Verity decided at length, looking round the room to see that it was reasonably tidy.

"Do you want me to stay?" asked Gillian when Erika had gone out.

"Why shouldn't you?"

Gillian shrugged. "Well, if it is a reporter, it might look more romantic if you kept it dark that you have a grown-up daughter."

Erika came in quickly to announce, "Mr. Nicholas Arundel."

He came in like a star actor making an entrance half-way through the first act. Charm was obviously one of Nick Arundel's main assets, and he did not hesitate to use it. Just over average height, he was well dressed in a stylish raglan overcoat, a Harris cloth suit of unusual colour and a maroon shirt with a dark green bow-tie. It was obvious at a glance that he followed one of the artistic professions.

"I am sorry to come barging in at this hour," he apologized with a charming smile, addressing himself to Verity, "I'm afraid I caught a dreadfully slow train."

Verity introduced herself and Gillian, then invited him to sit down. Obviously, he was not a newspaper reporter. "You have come down from town?" she inquired politely.

He nodded. "I'm a friend of your publisher, Bertram

Paskin," he explained. "We've known each other a long time."
He took a slim gold cigarette-case from his pocket and offered
them a choice of Turkish or Virginian.

"There's nothing wrong, is there?" queried Verity. "About
the book, I mean."

"Lord, no. Bertram tells me they're working night and day,
printing thousands of copies."

"Are you in the firm?" asked Verity.

He shook his head. "No. As a matter of fact, I'm a portrait
painter."

Verity looked puzzled. What possible purpose could a
portrait painter have in visiting her at nine o'clock in the
evening? She waited politely for him to go on.

"Bertram thought it would be a wonderful idea for me to
paint you, Mrs. Pleydell." He put as much expression into his
voice as a practised concert singer. It was a pleasant, light
baritone sort of voice, with a nice, mellow timbre of which he
was fully conscious.

"A portrait!" echoed Gillian, highly intrigued. She could
not think of any of her friends and acquaintances who had had
their portraits painted. Even the County families could not
afford such luxuries nowadays.

"I like to catch my subjects at exactly the right moment,"
Arundel went on to explain. "Probably that accounts for my
success. I always get them when they are right on the crest of
the wave—it gives them a sort of gloss. I caught Lucinda
Bayley after her big success in the new revue; Sir Woolfe
Farquharson just after he had discovered that special drug for
polio. . . . There is no doubt it makes a difference. Besides, a
portrait of somebody in the news always makes a good sale."

"You're one of these cubists?" demanded Verity anxiously.

He laughed, displaying two rows of small, well-spaced
teeth. "My work is practically photographic as far as the bone
structure is concerned," he reassured her. "I try to get most of
my distinctive effects with colouring."

Verity eyed him shrewdly. He seemed quite prosperous and
completely confident.

"I hadn't thought of having a portrait done," she admitted,
"It seems a bit premature. After all, you'd hardly describe me
as an established author."

"I've already explained that I like to catch people at the

start of their success," he countered. "Later on, they sometimes become cynical or bitter or spoilt . . . though I'm quite
sure it won't have that effect on you," he added hastily.

"Nice of you to say so," said Verity with a tiny smile,
wondering what he was thinking privately behind this chain
of compliments.

"Yes, the initial success always does something to people,"
he went on knowingly. "It rejuvenates them; brings a new
light into the eye, a different set of the chin, a certain assurance, an air of importance."

"Really, I don't feel very different," Verity said in a slightly
amused tone. "I am a bit excited of course, but this book isn't
everything. I have a lot of other interests."

"But you will have to take your writing more seriously
now," he smiled. "You have a duty to your new public.
They'll be on the lookout for your next book."

"I don't think my stuff is as wonderful as all that," replied
Verity, wondering vaguely what was the catch behind this
proposition. She offered him a cigarette and he sat back in his
chair and slowly expelled a long stream of smoke as he looked
round the room.

"It's very pleasant here," he decided. "Nice and restful.
You must get through an enormous amount of work."

"I have a lot of local interests," Verity informed him.

"Ah yes; Paskin told me your husband was one of the
local bigwigs."

"He's a bank manager, as a matter of fact."

"Very cosy."

Gilliam was eyeing the visitor in patent wonder. He was
something quite new in her experience. She had seen men like
him in plays and films, but could never quite believe in their
reality. Yet, there he was, large as life, smoking her father's
expensive cigarettes. . . .

"Yes, this part of the world would suit me very nicely,"
he was saying. "Interesting country, friendly people, good
shopping facilities, just enough entertainment, mellow old
hotels. . . . I've always said that life in a country town is my
ideal."

"Have you ever lived in a country town?" asked Gillian,
coming back to earth.

"No, I can't say I have. But I dare say I will before long.

London is becoming quite impossible these last few years. . . .
So wearing on the nerves, no peace, impossible to relax. I find
I can't work there half as well nowadays. That's why I paint
most of my sitters in their own homes."

Verity was still puzzled. Was he asking her to commission
a portrait, or had he a customer for her picture? Presently, he
stubbed out his cigarette with an elegant gesture and came to
business.

"I don't want you to misunderstand me, Mrs. Pleydell,"
he said, "I'm not touting for a commission to paint your
picture. Of course, if you felt you wanted to buy it when it was
finished, then I'd give you the first refusal. But that's entirely
up to you."

"And suppose no one else wants to buy it," suggested
Gillian.

"I have a feeling they will," he replied confidently. "I
rarely have any difficulty in selling this type of picture. You'd
be surprised what a difference it makes when the subject has
been prominently in the news and is on the way to becoming
a celebrity. That sort of picture usually fetches a good price,
particularly if it's painted in the home surroundings. In fact,
I think I can claim to have started something of a fashionable
demand for them."

Verity looked thoughtful. "You mean you would want to
paint me here?"

"Why not?"

"I—I don't know. It seems a little unusual."

"Not at all," said the artist. "I find I get much better
results when the subject is in her natural setting. She is able
to relax completely, and seeing her in the midst of her familiar
surroundings often gives me interesting ideas. I assure you it
works out wonderfully well."

"It would save mother travelling up and down to Town,"
Gillian pointed out in a practical tone. "And talking of
travelling, how are you getting back to London tonight?"
She looked at her wrist-watch. "The last train should be leaving just about now, if it's on time."

"Oh dear," said Verity. "What about the Green Line?"

"That went ten minutes ago."

"Don't worry, Mrs. Pleydell," said the artist. "I dare say
I'll find a bed in one of the local hotels without much trouble."

"We should have told you earlier about trains and things, but it hardly seemed polite," said Verity. "It's a shocking service on this line."

"I'll fix something," the visitor assured her. "At the moment I am more anxious about getting this question of your portrait all settled. I don't want you to make any promise you may regret later. I think you ought to take a look at some of my work; I've one or two things in the hall outside, if you'd like me to get them."

He half-rose, but Verity waved him back to his chair. "Ring for Erika, Gillian," she ordered. "She'll bring them in for you. Meanwhile, let's have a drink, shall we?"

He accepted a small whisky, and presently Erika came in answer to the bell. "Bring in Mr. Arundel's things from the hall," Verity told her.

When she had gone out, Verity turned to the visitor. "I've been thinking, Mr. Arundel, if you didn't object to rather a rough-and-ready arrangement, we have a small bedroom, a sort of semi-attic. It's nothing much, but the bed's comfortable."

"It sounds the sort of place I've often dreamt about," said Nick Arundel enthusiastically. "But don't let me upset your domestic arrangements; I can easily go to a hotel."

"They're all dreadful," put in Gillian quickly.

"Well, it's very kind of you, but I don't think I should presume on your hospitality. It was stupid of me not to think about return trains."

"Perfectly understandable," said Verity. "Londoners always expect trains to run till midnight."

"Then you'll stay?" interposed Gillian eagerly.

Before he could reply, the door opened to admit Erika, who carried a large suitcase in either hand and had a small easel tucked under one arm and a large leather portfolio under the other. It had obviously taken her some time to assume her burden. Mr. Arundel had apparently come prepared to make a long stay.

"Where shall I put them, Mrs. Pleydell?" asked Erika, and when she had gone the artist turned to his hostess and said:

"There's one thing I forgot, Mrs. Pleydell. I'm afraid I'm practically a vegetarian."

CHAPTER VII

FUN TO BE FAMOUS

WITH the sale of every extra ten thousand copies of *The Passionate Mirage*, Pleydell became more and more despondent. It wasn't only having a comparative stranger living with the family and littering his painting outfit all over the place; nor even having to find alternative garage accommodation for his car, while his own garage housed the new shining blue roadster. It wasn't only the vegetarian diet which persistently disagreed with him. The main reason for his disquiet lay in the fact that he was persistently reminded that he was not the master in his own house.

His family seemed to take it for granted that because his wife's income was somewhere around five times his own, and would shortly, with the sale of the film rights of the book, soar to even more fantastic heights, she was now the monarch of all she surveyed in the Pleydell *ménage*. It wasn't natural, he gloomily reflected. If a man can't assert himself under his own roof, then his self-confidence is undermined. Once a woman got the bit fairly between her teeth, she never knew when to stop. That was why it would never do to let a woman take over a bank manager's job; not a single client would have any faith in her.

Of course, Verity had always been burdened with an excess of vitality, and he had made due allowance for the fact, though it had meant giving her her head at times and letting her go her own way. Once she had exhausted the particular craze she was intent upon, things quickly returned to normal.

But this best-seller novelist phase was far more formidable than anything that had happened before, and had much wider repercussions. Verity had become a celebrity, and appeared to bathe in an amber limelight wherever she went. When his clients and acquaintances mentioned her, a noticeable new note came into their voices, as if she were now on that remote plane inhabited by actresses who are interviewed at the Savoy Hotel and film stars who are photographed at film *premières*.

As the sales of the book rocketed towards the hundred

thousand mark, Verity seemed to get less and less time for anyone. That young fellow Nick Arundel found it difficult to persuade her to fit him in even for an odd hour in two days, and she was rushing up to London at least three or four times a week. The rather peculiar acquaintances she made up there had descended upon them once or twice at week-ends, and Pleydell couldn't feel very enthusiastic about them. They certainly were not the type with whom he would want to do business.

Verity was very much in demand for literary luncheons, lectures and public appearances at book departments in the larger stores. He supposed this whirl would subside sometime; otherwise she would never get down to writi g a sequel. Maybe that would not be such a bad thing, he reflected, for he did not relish the idea of living the rest of his life at this tempo.

However, he had to admit that Verity revelled in it. She was like an actress who had at last made a big success in a star part that suited her to perfection. There was no holding her. She was like a big business man who went round telling people his time was worth a pound a minute; you felt you ought to pay a fee to speak to her.

Of course, it was just an episode, Pleydell kept reassuring himself, but he could see no immediate possibility of its coming to an end. In fact, one thing kept leading to another; her circle was continually widening like the ripples from a stone thrown into a pond. She had about as much time for family life as an M.P. when the House was in session.

Maybe it was because all this fuss came at a critical period in her life, but the fact remained that it seemed to have accentuated some of her faults and negatived her good qualities. For instance, she was no longer cautious about money; she spent every penny she earned, sometimes before she received it. She bought dresses that did not suit her and things for the house that she never used; something seemed to be driving her to spend money as if that were now part of her way of life.

It was useless to venture any sort of protest, for Verity never seemed to have time to listen to anybody in her home circle; she was so busy with her letters and telegrams and telephone calls from London. If they all had a meal together, it was sure to be interrupted.

Pleydell suspected that even the artist chap was getting a bit fed up with the whole thing, though of course he knew when he was well off. He appeared to be paying rather a lot of attention to Gillian; that was another worry. He couldn't be there to watch them all the time. The girl's mother should do something about it, instead of encouraging the young fellow to be for ever lounging about the place. In fact, the more Pleydell thought about his home affairs, the more complicated they seemed to become, and it was with a positive feeling of relief that he turned to the comparatively straightforward problems that confronted him at the bank.

Up to a point, Nick Arundel enjoyed idling, but after a time it palled upon him and he became bored. So that when Verity was away on one of her many expeditions, he began to amuse himself by sketching a profile of Gillian. She was an interesting subject, though she lacked her mother's animation. She had the family's slightly prominent high cheek-bones, and rather unusual eyes, set widely apart . . . he liked the tilt of her chin too, and the sweep of the hair from the forehead. He was just getting the chin right when she turned her head slightly and spoiled the angle.

"Damn! You've moved again!" he protested.

"Sorry," she said, trying to recapture the original pose. "That better?"

"No, that's too much."

"I'll get a crick in my neck if I hold this much longer," she told him. "Thank goodness I don't have to earn a living this way."

"You never said a truer word," he agreed absently, intent on his sketch. "The pay's rotten too . . . wouldn't keep you in nylons."

"I sometimes think I'd like to be independent," she murmured almost to herself.

He rubbed out a line rather violently and blew the shreds of rubber away. "Take it from me, it's absolute hell being independent," he informed her. "At least it is if you have no money."

"That's why I think I'd like to earn some."

"You don't know when you are well off. You've a comfortable home, plenty of friends, and as much pocket money as you need."

"It isn't quite as rosy as all that."

"It might be lots worse. Head back a bit, if you can manage it . . . thanks."

She wondered when this sitting would end. At first, she had felt vaguely flattered, but he seemed to lose himself so much in the work that he wasn't nearly as interesting. Presently, he told her she could rest for a few minutes.

"I've always meant to ask you," she said, now she had his full attention, "about these girl models."

He sighed. It was the old, old question; like the author being asked where he found his plots, or the actor how he achieved his make-up. "You mean about the girls who pose in the nude?" he said wearily. "Most of them are rather less interesting than an intelligent carthorse."

"But there are one or two," she persisted, accepting a light for her cigarette.

"Maybe one or two," he conceded. "And they invariably have a husband or a lover. I don't think you'd make a fortune posing in the nude, if that's what's worrying you," he added with a grin.

"You think I haven't the figure?"

"On the contrary, I think you have a remarkably good figure. I wouldn't mind doing a full-length of you. But you wouldn't make big money at posing because the money simply isn't there. Much better to go on the films."

"That means acting," she said with a tiny shrug.

"Sort of," he agreed.

"I don't know whether I'd be any good. Of course I've done some local amateur dramatics."

"Yes, you told me," he put in quickly. "Taken on the whole, I think I'd advise you to stay at home and have lots of fun with the local boys."

"But you don't know the local boys."

He shrugged. "Men are pretty much the same wherever you go."

"They can't all be as dreary as this sporting crowd," she insisted. "I honestly don't know how you've put up with them all these weeks."

"But I haven't seen very much of them, and I like it here. Your father's easy to get on with; your mother's very stimulating; and you—well, you're nice to see around the place."

E

"You might say the same about Erika," she pouted.

"In a different sort of way," he agreed. "But you have a much better profile. Shall we begin again?"

"I don't suppose Mother will approve of your doing this," she told him, as she resumed the pose. "What's going to happen about her picture?" She indicated the canvas which stood on an easel in the corner under an old dust-cover.

"It's coming along," he said. "But she gets so little time for sitting, and I'm rather a slow worker."

"Yes, she's hardly ever at home since the book was published. I sometimes suspect that she goes round the bookshops asking them how many copies they've sold."

He laughed. "She's too busy lecturing and making her personal appearances. But she really is a difficult subject for a painter; she's so restless. There are times when I feel like giving it up; I've really trespassed far too long on your hospitality."

"Good heavens, you mustn't think of it," she protested. "We all like having you here; the place would be quite dull without you."

"All the same, I've a feeling your mother's getting a bit bored with the portrait. And I don't suppose your father wants a stranger about the place indefinitely."

"But you aren't a stranger any longer. We look on you almost as part of the family. I'm surprised you're not bored with us."

He smiled. "It's pleasant to live in a well-ordered household. My life was a bit haphazard in that respect."

She rested on her elbows and eyed him thoughtfully as he busied himself at his drawing-pad. He was wearing a pale blue open-necked shirt and a maroon pullover. His dark hair was ruffled and his grey flannel trousers had one or two smears of paint on them. From time to time he pursed his lips and squinted critically at his drawing.

"You live by yourself in Chelsea?" inquired Gillian.

"Since my wife and I agreed to separate about three years ago."

"You never told us about that."

"Nothing much to tell. We simply agreed to differ and decided we'd be happier apart. All very sordid really."

"And what is she doing now?"

"Living by her wits, as far as I know. Aren't we all?"

"Don't you have to make her an allowance?"

He shook his head. "She knows she wouldn't have much chance of getting it. When we were together she often earned more money than I did. She was pretty adaptable really— tackled all sorts of jobs, from mannequin to hotel receptionist. She's one of those girls who seem able to walk into a job whenever they feel like it."

He held his drawing away from himself for a moment, then went on working furiously. Apparently he was not inclined to discuss his domestic affairs any further. She, too, felt no great urge to talk. The news that he was married came as a shock. She could feel her heart beating; it throbbed unpleasantly in her ears and she had some difficulty in maintaining her pose. However, he did not seem to notice her reaction, but went on sketching as industriously as ever.

Gillian tried to survey the situation dispassionately, but found it difficult. He was something new and exciting in her life, and she was more than half in love with him. She didn't know how she would exist when he finished the portrait. Maybe it would be possible to see him in Town, but the approach would have to come from him. And she was none too sure he was that interested in her. But he had opened her eyes to strange new worlds, and now there was no turning back. Or so it seemed in the urgency of that moment.

"Haven't you—wouldn't she want a divorce?" she asked after a long pause.

"Eh? You mean my wife?" he said absently. "Oh, I dare say we might get round to it one day. Divorce is damned expensive you know."

For several minutes he went on sketching in silence. Probably he isn't the marrying type, thought Gillian, who had so often read in modern novels that people with the artistic temperament should not tie themselves to a permanent partner. It was all very bewildering. Of course, if he loved some other woman desperately, she might have the power over him to insist on marriage.

At length she said: "You've flattered my chin. It sticks out more than that."

"That shows a determined nature," he said. "Your mother's is the same."

"Well, Daddy's isn't. And after all, he is a bank manager."

"Does that require determination, or just influence?" inquired Nick.

"That I couldn't say. Daddy never tells us much about bank affairs. Still, you have to remember that there are 20,000 clerks in this bank and only 1,600 managers. He's told us that much at any rate."

"So you know very little about banking?"

"Practically nothing. What was it you wanted to know?"

"Oh, nothing very much. I must admit I've been curious occasionally as to how some friends of mine have managed to get an overdraft. Personally, I wouldn't have lent 'em a penny."

"I understand that luck plays a large part in it," she gravely informed him.

He laughed. "I'm sure the Governor of the Bank of England would be interested to hear that."

He went on sketching steadily, and presently Erika came in with some coffee, which she set out on a small table, then came and peeped over Nick's shoulder. "It is very beautiful," she said admiringly.

"She means it flatters me," smiled Gillian.

Erika shook her head vigorously. "It would be very nice for the cover of the *Modern Girl* magazine," she decided, awarding the highest praise she knew.

"Oh lord," said Nick dolefully, "is it as bad as that?"

Gillian laughed and started to pour out the coffee.

"I have not said the right thing?" queried Erika anxiously.

"Don't worry, Erika," said Gillian. "I know I would be thrilled to see my picture on a magazine cover."

"We must see if it can be arranged," said Nick, thoughtfully stirring his coffee. Then he sipped it with obvious relish, which she noted.

"You're breaking your vegetarian resolutions," she told him. "It isn't dandelion coffee. It's the genuine article."

"Still, a vegetable product," he shrugged. "Though of course the cranks don't approve of it."

"I always make the coffee when I am at home," Erika told them. "Everyone say I make very good coffee. It is an old family recipe that I use this morning. I will teach it to you if you like, Miss Gillian. When you are living with a man it is nice to know how to make good coffee. It will always put him in a sweet temper."

She giggled selfconsciously and went off to the kitchen. Nick lighted another cigarette and Gillian sat back in her chair with her hands clasped behind her head. It had been stupid of her to get upset when she heard he was married. After all, one could hardly expect a man to reach his age, living an artist's life, without some knowledge of the opposite sex. If she had been really sophisticated, she would have taken it for granted.

"I hope the coffee won't interfere with your work," she said.

"Not at all. I feel like a new man."

"Have some more." She refilled his cup. "Erika's funny, isn't she? She talked as if it were a sort of love potion."

"Very quaint," he murmured, hardly having heard what she had said. He was busy again with his work.

"She seems to have had a lot of experience with men," Gillian continued, with a smothered sigh.

"Not surprising, really," frowned Nick, exhaling smoke. "Particularly if she was in Holland during the two occupations."

"Anyway, she seems quite pleased about it. No complaints."

"Perfectly natural," he nodded, shading vigorously.

Gillian narrowed her lips. Obviously he wasn't very interested in the conversation. But something drove her on. "I can't think why she doesn't go back to Holland," she said rather petulantly. "She seemed to have a very good time there."

"Maybe she's doing pretty well here."

She looked at him shrewdly. Once or twice she had thought he was on slightly too-friendly terms with Erika. She had heard them laughing on the stairs, and seen them occasionally exchange an intimate glance. And now she came to think of it, Erika was always reticent about her half-days and evenings out. Resolutely, she put the suspicion from her mind and stiffened into the pose once more.

"You don't often work like this," she murmured.

"I'm not often in the mood."

"Then I suppose we must make the most of it."

He nodded absent-mindedly and rubbed out a tiny line at the corner of her mouth.

"I've thought once or twice it must be rather fun to go to an art school," she ventured.

"Believe me, it's nothing of the sort. At least, not if you really want to draw or paint."

"I don't see why. Did you go to one?"

"I've been chucked out of four in my time. But don't let me put you off, if you think you'd like to paint pretty things on home-made vases."

"One has to start somewhere," she argued.

"There are many more exciting ways of passing the time."

He stubbed out his cigarette with an impatient gesture and frowned at his drawing more fiercely than ever.

"You have quite a pleasant life," she insisted. "You'll meet all sorts of celebrities; it must be quite interesting."

"It rather depends on the celebrity," he sniffed. "Some of them can be pretty nerve-racking."

"Anyhow you're on to a good line. I wouldn't be a bit surprised if you ended up as an R.A."

"I hope I don't paint that sort of portrait."

"And one day you'll write a book about how people stood up to the limelight of fame."

"I might if I could spell," he grinned. "And I'll see you get an honourable mention."

At that moment Verity came in wearing her hat and coat. She went straight to her desk and took out her diary, which she pored over for two or three minutes, then said, "I can give you a quarter of an hour before lunch, Nick, if you like."

"Are you out to lunch again?" asked Gillian.

"Yes, I told you. It's the affair at the Guildhall for the encouragement of tourists."

"Oh yes, I remember now. Is Daddy going?"

"Of course. He's vice-chairman of the Chamber of Commerce, and they are running it. Put that away, Nick, and let's make a start."

"I'm sorry, but a quarter of an hour is really no use at all," he said bluntly."

Verity looked faintly annoyed. "I don't see why," she said. "I often turn out a few hundred words when I have ten minutes to spare. It all helps, you know."

"You should know by now it takes me that long to get properly settled down," he replied. "By the time I've mixed my colours and got everything ready, you'll have to go. It's happened several times before."

Verity gave vent to an exclamation and began pacing up and down the room restlessly. She need not start for at least twenty minutes, and there was nothing for her to do. Of course, she could have done a little work on the new book, but for once in a way she was not in the mood.

"Is there any coffee left?" she asked presently.

"Oh yes," replied Gillian. "It's still hot." She poured a cup and passed it to her mother.

"What are you and Nick doing today?" she inquired.

"I'm playing tennis this afternoon; it's the start of the hard court tournament," said Gillian.

"And you, Nick?"

"I might do a bit of work on your picture. There's one or two touches on the dress to get right."

"I'd no idea it took so long to finish a picture," said Verity, stirring her coffee.

"Quite often it doesn't."

"I'm dying to see how it turns out," she admitted. "This is very good coffee, though it has rather a different taste."

"Yes," smiled Gillian. "It really is coffee. I bought a pound; I couldn't stand dandelions any longer."

Verity set down her cup. "I don't think I should drink it," she said dubiously.

"It's quite harmless," Nick assured her.

"It's very bad for the heart . . . or the liver. I don't remember which."

"But it's very good for the morale," Nick smiled. "Erika made it from an old Dutch recipe."

"Well, I suppose it's a shame to waste it," said Verity, taking another appreciative sip. It really was excellent coffee, with all its rich flavour and none of the bitter taste that seemed so inevitable in English hotels and restaurants.

"All the same," said Verity, "we've been getting rather lax about the health diet just these last few weeks."

"It's all right for you," said Gillian. "You're always out at luncheons and dinners. You can stoke up."

"I do no such thing!" declared her mother indignantly. "I always refuse the meat dishes."

With a sigh, Nick pushed aside his drawing-board and

flung down his pencil. Verity peered at the drawing. "H'm . . . not a very good likeness, is it?" she commented.

"Perhaps not," said Gillian, "but it's a lovely picture. . . . May I keep it?" she added, turning to Nick. He shook his head and said he would like to finish it sometime when he was in the mood. He slipped the sketch inside his portfolio and went and stared out of the window.

"I think you should go for a nice walk as it is such a lovely morning," suggested Verity. "You can come with me if you like. I'm walking into the town to get some exercise. It stirs up the brain and gives you new ideas."

"All right," agreed Nick. "I'll go and put on a tie. There's several things I want to get in Firbright."

Verity rang for Erika to take away the coffee tray, and Gillian was going into the garden when her mother called her back. "Just a minute, Gillian dear."

Gillian turned and looked at her. What's on her mind this time, she thought.

"There's something I want to talk to you about," said Verity, perching on the arm of a chair. "That's another new dress you are wearing," she added inconsequently.

"Yes, I got it on Thursday when I was in Town."

"You never mentioned it."

"I don't seem to have seen much of you lately," Gillian reminded her. "You've been away most of the time. And it only cost eleven guineas; I'm still inside my allowance. You've had two new outfits since I got my blue evening——"

"Never mind about that now," interrupted Verity, "I want to talk to you about Nick."

CHAPTER VIII

MOTHERLY ADVICE

ERIKA came in and collected the coffee cups. As she was walking out with the tray she stopped and asked, "Could I have this evening off, Mrs. Pleydell?"

"But Thursday is your night," said Verity.

"That's right, Mrs. Pleydell, but a friend asked me to go to the theatre with him this evening."

Once again, Gillian felt a vague pang of jealousy and fear combined. She dared not ask Erika if she were going to the theatre with Nick. "Very well, Erika," she heard her mother say, "I daresay we'll manage somehow."

Erika thanked her and went out with the tray.

"Another of her gentleman friends, I suppose," said Gillian with an attempt at light-heartedness as soon as the door closed.

"One can't be too strict with her," said Verity, "or she'll just get the next boat for Holland."

"That girl always seems to get the best of all worlds."

Verity shrugged impatiently. She was not very keen to discuss Erika. "It's Nick I want to talk to you about," she began.

"You think it's time he finished your picture?"

"I haven't really thought about that. But I feel I ought to warn you about him."

"In what way?"

Verity hesitated. It was about ten years since she had enlightened her daughter about the origins of the human race, and she had felt little need to supplement the information since then. However it was not going to be easy to warn her about a man whom she had herself invited to be a guest in the house. Still, Verity always had a certain sense of duty; there were things which had to be gone through with, like the agenda at a committee meeting. She took the plunge.

"You two have been together rather a lot lately and you are just at the age when a girl thinks artists are romantic and all that sort of thing."

"You can't deny they're more romantic than bank clerks," retorted Gillian with just a trace of acerbity.

Verity rushed quickly into the breach. "I'm not saying there's anything wrong. But he is very charming, and plenty of girls might misunderstand him."

"You needn't worry about that," Gillian assured her. "He hasn't even tried to hold my hand."

But Verity was still worried. "All the same, I wish he'd hurry up and finish the picture," she confessed. "When I give him extra sittings he seems to wipe out as much as he paints. I often wonder if he's really as good as he makes out."

"He once had a picture hung at the Academy."

"Really? He never told me."

"I think he's a bit ashamed of it. He said it was before he knew very much about painting. And they hung it so high it was almost out of sight."

Verity stirred uneasily in her chair. "There's something about him I can't understand," she admitted. "I have a feeling I should ask him to go. After all, he's been here ten weeks."

"That isn't such a long time to complete a real work of art."

"I wrote my novel in twelve," said Verity assertively, as if that settled the question once and for all. Gillian did not like to suggest that it was hardly the same thing.

"Anyhow," Verity went on, "he can't stay here very much longer. I've already wasted far too much time on sitting for this portrait. I must have a quiet talk to him and see if he has any future plans. If he doesn't finish that picture soon, people will begin to talk."

At that moment the subject of their conversation strolled in, looking extremely presentable in a new suit and an Artillery tie, which he assured them he had no right to wear, but which he had acquired because he delighted to wear it with a salmon shirt.

He seemed to have changed his mood with his clothes. Before they left the house he had complimented Verity on her hat and her new handbag, and chatted away so divertingly on their walk across the fields that she could never contrive to bring the conversation round to the subject of his leaving. When she mentioned the portrait, he assured her that it would soon be finished and immediately started to talk about something else.

Verity went into the bank to call for her husband, and Nick to a stationer's that stocked artists' materials. In the bank she found Pleydell in his office looking rather pale and worried. "Are you ready?" she asked. "It's nearly a quarter-to, and we ought to be at the hotel to receive the visitors. I believe there are several people coming from Town. . . ."

Pleydell nodded.

"Is anything wrong?" asked Verity.

"I've had a bit of a shock. You'd better come back here with me after the dinner and we'll have a talk about it."

"You mean it's something to do with me?"

"It certainly is. You're the entire cause of it," he informed her.

"Can't we settle it now?"

"There won't be time." He went over to the cupboard where he kept his hat and coat.

"I'm not overdrawn again, am I?"

"Not as far as I know. We'd better go or we'll be late."

He was evasive throughout their short walk to the Plough Hotel, where the luncheon was being held. They found over fifty people there, most of them in the bar, where there was a pleasant hum of conversation. Pleydell exchanged greetings with several of his clients, evaded several others for whom he would had to have bought expensive drinks, and steered Verity in the direction of the Firbright Tourist Bureau.

When they all moved into the luncheon-room, Pleydell was somewhat mortified to see that his wife was sitting at the top of the chairman's table, while he was at a side table some distance down the room. However, it was too late to protest, and, after all, the managers of Lloyds and Barclays banks were no better placed. Not that Pleydell particularly wanted this Tourist Bureau account. In his experience, they were always more trouble than they were worth. Their only value lay in the fact that they sometimes provided useful connections with the officials on the committee, and, of course, there was some slight prestige attached to being treasurer of a local organization.

It was the usual type of three-course lunch provided for the Rotary Club, who met each week in the same room. Afterwards there were three short speeches, from the chairman, the secretary and Verity, as a preliminary to the pep talk from a stocky little man with a cleft chin and piercing eyes who was introduced as the deputy director-general of the British Tourist League. His name was Ridgeway, and he was of Scottish origin, though he did his utmost to conceal the fact, chiefly by adopting a slick American intonation in his speech.

Ridgeway informed them in no uncertain manner that he was out for dollars. It was his job to attract the American tourists, and he left no stones unturned. He gave them to understand that he knew more about the likes and dislikes of

American visitors than any man in the country; hence his present position.

It seemed that first and foremost the Americans craved Comfort with a capital C. But if it was not possible to give them a bathroom to every bedroom and ice on every table, then at least they must be given Service, emphasized Mr. Ridgeway, dramatically thumping the table. However intent they may be upon their daily shopping, the ladies of Firbright must make it their business to stop and enlighten the inquiring visitor as to the local beauty spots; the time and place the Firbright Hunt met; the ancient history of the town and the route to Stratford-upon-Avon. It was, said Mr. Ridgeway, only a question of educating people.

He went on to quote figures—how many hundred thousand Americans reached us every summer, laden with so many millions of dollars. In fact, London had reached saturation point. Some of the Yanks had got to be tempted into the outlying areas, places such as Firbright, which were reeking with old traditions and could put on a show for the tourists. The British Tourist League would help them to improve their hotels and to obtain permits to raise the general standard of catering. In his peroration Mr. Ridgeway emphasized that not only would they be adding to their profits; they would be doing a real job for Britain in winning hard-earned dollars for her.

The speaker sat down amidst considerable applause and there was a certain amount of discussion as to ways and means, followed by the formation of sub-committees. The meeting did not break up until nearly two-thirty, and five minutes later Verity was sitting opposite her husband in his room at the bank.

He had asked her there because he felt much more at home in that familiar office when he had to talk business. His home surroundings were quite different; he was much 'softer' there when discussing financial affairs. In fact, he avoided doing so as far as possible, and never encouraged clients to call at his house when they wanted to discuss banking matters.

There was something reassuring about the flat, leather-topped desk, with its telephone, writing-pad and elaborate ink-stand, the 'in' and 'out' trays, the small pile of reference books on the shelf, the neat hearth and the rich mahogany panelling.

With his back to the window, and the customer facing the light, Pleydell was in as strong a position as any man could wish. He could even face his own wife with a certain confidence.

He opened a drawer and took out his reading glasses, then unlocked another drawer inside which, on top of some documents, was a small scrap of paper, covered with figures.

"I haven't much time," said Verity, glancing at the clock on the mantelpiece. "There's a committee meeting of the Inner Wheel at four, and I've some shopping to do. . . ."

"I'm sorry," said Pleydell rather more assertively than usual, "but this may take quite a time. And it's very important. Wilkinson came in this morning about a little matter, and after we'd settled it we started chatting about other things."

"You mean Wilkinson the Income Tax inspector?" she queried, and Pleydell nodded. She hated Wilkinson, with his tooth-brush moustache and oily manner. She never forgot his relating to her how a bus conductor had once boasted to him how he made an extra thirty shillings a week out of breeding rabbits, and how he had taken his number and sent him a new demand form before the week was out. That was Wilkinson. At the first mention of money in any gossiping circle he pricked up his ears. He couldn't have been more assiduous if he were the Chancellor of the Exchequer.

"What did he want?" demanded Verity. "We don't owe him anything, do we?"

"Not yet," replied Pleydell quietly. Something in his tone made her turn quickly.

"You mean he's been snooping?" she asked.

"He read a bit in the *Morning News* about you making over five thousand so far out of the book and about that twenty-thousand offer for the film rights."

Verity played with the clasp of her bag, snapping it open and shut. "But surely you told him these figures are exaggerated in the newspapers for publicity purposes. It isn't evidence, and nobody can prove it."

"He can demand to see your banking account, and I'll have to show it to him. Mind, I'm not saying he will, but there's always a chance. I am bound to make a statement of your earnings on my return, or there'll be the devil to pay with the bank. And Wilkinson knows that well enough."

"What did he say exactly?"

"Nothing definite; he put on that joking tone of his. Just giving me a pretty strong hint about the position."

"But it's *my* money," she insisted.

"I'm quite aware of that," he replied stiffly. "But you happen to be my wife, and I have to declare your income on my return." He consulted the slip of paper on his desk. "I drafted out a few figures, and they're rather startling, Verity. As Wilkinson pointed out, with your earnings on the top of mine—and my unearned income as well—I shall be right up in the super-taxed class. As far as I can see, I shall be paying at least fifteen shillings in the pound."

"That's ridiculous!" she protested.

"It means I shall be called on to hand over more money than I can lay my hands on. Even if the bank allowed me an overdraft."

Verity frowned. Of course, it would be all right if she sold the film rights, though several people had warned her not to depend on that until she had the cheque safely in the bank. And she had been spending rather heavily lately. In addition to the car, she had bought horses for herself and Gillian at a local riding stable, paid a deposit on a flat in Town which would shortly fall vacant at a rent of £500 a year, and run up dress bills approaching four figures. She had received around £3,000 so far from her publishers, and her account was overdrawn a few pounds. Then there was the houseboat she had contemplated buying at Maidenhead. She had half-promised to take it, and the owner was holding it for her. . . . There seemed to be no ending to her commitments. And she had not paid a penny income tax yet.

"It all seems most unfair," she said. "I'd no idea the tax would be so heavy."

"No more had I. . . . At least, it hadn't occurred to me. But Wilkinson seemed to have it all nicely worked out."

Verity sniffed. "I bet he was rubbing his hands in that objectionable way of his. Anybody would think he got a commission."

"I don't suppose he often makes a haul of this size."

A clock struck three and the outer doors of the bank closed with a distant thud. There was a clatter of scales on the counter outside as the cashiers began weighing their silver and copper. There came a tap on the door and a typist entered with some letters for signature, which she placed in one of the trays. Verity rolled her expensive new suède gloves into a shapeless ball.

"Well," she said at last, "what are we going to do?"

"I'm damned if I know," replied Pleydell frankly. "I suppose we'll just have to wait and see what they demand."

"I can't think why it should be so much."

"It wouldn't be, if you were paying it yourself as a single woman. It's when it comes on top of my salary and the unearned income from Cousin Oliver's legacy that it jumps into the super-tax class. You'll have to cut down your spending or we're going to be in very deep water." He reached over and pulled the pile of letters towards him, carefully scanning the top one before signing it and flicking it into the 'out' tray.

They argued for nearly half an hour without coming any nearer to a solution, and succeeded only in irritating each other profoundly. Verity resented being accused of extravagance; she considered that she had a right to money she earned, and it seemed to her the height of injustice that her husband should be heavily taxed on it.

Pleydell, for his part, was more than a little alarmed at this sudden tendency to uninhibited spending on the part of his wife, and thought, as the financial expert in the partnership, she might have consulted him. He sent for the statement of her banking account, which showed that it was £12 overdrawn, and that she had issued cheques to the value of nearly £500 in the past fortnight. It was quite frightening.

He knew from past experience that the fatherly lecture he reserved for his clients on the question of curtailing expenditure would not take effect with Verity, whose acid tongue could side-track him into a dozen personal issues that really had very little connection with the main burden of his argument. He was sorry now that he had allowed her to open a separate banking account a few years back; he had felt some misgivings about it at the time, though he had to admit that it had worked reasonably well until she had begun to earn those fantastic sums of money. When that happened, women seemed to lose all sense of proportion.

All through her committee meeting, Verity's mind was continually wandering from the agenda. The thought of the oleaginous Mr. Wilkinson nagged at her like an aching tooth. How dare he come counting his chickens before Andrew was even due to make a new income tax return? It was monstrous!

As the meeting progressed, she found herself becoming more and more murderously inclined towards the unwitting Mr. Wilkinson, who at that moment was busily engaged upon issuing four summonses for amounts varying from two-and-fourpence to six shillings.

Of course, a woman in her position could not assassinate officials of Her Majesty's Government, but she could not allow herself to be victimized in this manner. It was nothing short of that. Mechanically, she seconded resolutions and raised her hand to vote on this and that motion. She even made a very short speech. But her thoughts boomeranged time and again to the question of super-tax. That there was, technically, no longer any such thing as super-tax made no difference. She thought of it in those terms. Andrew was too fearful of his position to put up much of a fight. He might appeal against these crazy demands, but he would not venture to do anything that was in the least unorthodox. All sorts of alternatives leapt into her mind. They could go to live in Jersey, where the tax was negligible . . . but Andrew would never give up his job. He could issue a public disclaimer of his wife's debts . . . but of course he would never have the nerve. Her brain wheeled with one plan after another, but there seemed to be a flaw in all of them.

It was not until she was walking back across the fields that the idea struck her. She stopped at the next stile and leaned against it for nearly five minutes, lost in thought.

The idea seemed to be foolproof all right. Of course, it was unorthodox, and it would take courage. Andrew would almost certainly fight shy of it, but she would have to assert herself. The situation was urgent and called for desperate remedies . . . and maybe if she led the way successfully thousands of other women would follow suit. It might even build up to another suffragette campaign, with herself at the head. It would be wonderful publicity; front-page lead in all the papers.

Then another thought struck her. Perhaps it would be as well if there were as little fuss as possible. It would be safer to take no chances until the whole thing was a *fait accompli*. If it got into the hands of the income tax people's solicitors, they might easily find a flaw. . . .

She walked briskly on.

This affair would be open to all sorts of complications; she would have to use a lot of discretion. At the same time, she would have to be firm.

When she got home, she rang up her poulterer, whom she had not patronized for weeks, and asked him if he could send a nice plump chicken round immediately. That would help to get Andrew in a mellow frame of mind. She did not intend to let that creature Wilkinson get the better of her without a struggle.

CHAPTER IX

VERITY MAKES A PROPOSITION

VERITY had not cooked a meal for several weeks, for Gillian usually deputized when Erika was out. On this occasion, however, her mother insisted on cooking the chicken herself. There was a warm, appetizing smell already drifting from the kitchen when Pleydell got home soon after six.

He sniffed suspiciously. "That smells uncommonly like chicken," he said to Gillian, who was practising a new dance step to the radio.

"Any objections?" she inquired.

"It wouldn't be another of these new-fangled vegetable substitutes, would it? Or is Erika entertaining her young man?"

"Erika is out, and Mother's cooking a real chicken."

"Someone coming to dinner then?"

"Not as far as I know."

"You mean we're going to have a whole chicken to ourselves? Just the four of us?"

"It looks as if there'll only be three. Nick hasn't got back yet."

"Humph . . . what's happened to him?"

"He went with Mother into town to get some colours and things. Erika's taking her night off at the theatre."

F

Pleydell went and poured himself a drink. He looked round somewhat furtively, then came over to Gillian and said in a conspiratorial tone, "Has she decided to stop the vegetarian nonsense?"

"She hasn't said anything to me," replied Gillian. "And I haven't asked her."

He nodded approvingly. "That's right . . . best not to say anything. Let her come round in her own way. Otherwise she's liable to get stubborn and stick to her principles."

They exchanged a knowing smile.

All the same, Pleydell was puzzled that Verity, after receiving that setback about super-tax, should rush home and start cooking a chicken. However, there was no accounting for women. He recalled Nick telling him about an actress friend who, whenever she just failed to get a part, would rush out and buy the most expensive new hat she could afford.

Taken all round, it was best to let domestic events shape their own course, and thankfully accept any small benefits. In the long run, life was less harassing that way. It was quite enough, as far as he was concerned, to guide the conduct of over two thousand banking accounts.

He had been racking his brains all afternoon to find some way out of this income tax impasse, but, unlike his wife, he had not reached even a glimmer of a solution. As far as he could see, the only way out would be to stall and ask for time to pay, but he didn't trust Wilkinson, who was the type who blurted out confidences to people in a position to make trouble. More than once he had tried to pump him about the affairs of his clients—of course, it had all been done in an offhand, casual way—but it was obvious what Wilkinson was after.

When he had business with the income tax office, Pleydell usually avoided Wilkinson and interviewed Stanford, his superior officer, who was always courteous and businesslike and ready to be reasonable. Maybe he ought to go and have a chat with Stanford during the next week or so. Gloomily, he poured himself another drink. The whole business hardly bore thinking about. That one should be reduced almost to poverty because one's wife wrote a best-seller novel! He could hardly believe they were living in England at all. It was the sort of thing you heard the American anti-communist propaganda broadcasts describing as happening behind the Iron Curtain.

With an effort, he wrenched his mind back to the more immediate future. "Are you going out tonight?" he asked Gillian.

"Yes, it's dancing club night. I'm going with Harold."

"I thought you hadn't been there very much lately."

"I haven't; but Harold 'phoned this afternoon. He seemed quite anxious to go."

He eyed her keenly. "How are you getting on with Harold lately?" he wanted to know. "Still feel the same about him?"

"Pretty much the same," she answered, wondering vaguely if that were really true. Would she have agreed to go dancing with him if Nick hadn't told her this morning about being married? She kicked herself mentally. What on earth has that got to do with it? she asked herself. But it was nagging away there at the back of her mind.

"Of course, Harold isn't what you might call an exciting type," mused Pleydell. "But he's steady—very steady. If you did marry him, you'd be the boss, of course. And I don't know if that's entirely a good thing," he added hastily. "All depends on the point of view, I suppose."

"I've no intention of marrying him. We happen to have learned dancing together, and our steps suit each other."

"But you can't fool me that he doesn't want something more than that. He's practically asked my permission."

"And what did you say?"

"I told him it was none of my business really, but if he could persuade you, I should offer no objections."

Before they could explore the subject any further, Verity called to Gillian to help her in the kitchen, and Pleydell sank into his favourite armchair, where he moodily studied the melodramatic contents of the evening paper.

He was careful to compliment Verity on the excellent meal, without making any direct reference to the question of the chicken. Whether the poulterer had been anxious for the renewal of Mrs. Pleydell's custom, she didn't know, but he had certainly sent up a lusciously tender bird. It was a pleasure to carve it.

Immediately afterwards, Gillian piled up the dishes in the kitchen and retired upstairs to change, while Pleydell returned to his armchair feeling much more reasonably disposed towards mankind. "That's what I call a really satisfying meal," he announced. "You can't beat home cooking, whatever these hotel people and restaurateurs may say."

A car horn sounded outside, and presently they heard Gillian running downstairs.

"That'll be Harold, I suppose," said Pleydell.

"Yes, I'm glad they're going out," murmured Verity. "It'll do her good. And we'll be able to have a nice, quiet chat."

"Gillian put her head round the door to tell them she would not be late, and a second later they heard the front door bang.

"I wish she'd learn not to slam doors," frowned Pleydell. "It's all so unnecessary."

It was one of his favourite complaints that a woman could never leave a room without making a dramatic exit and banging the door after her to draw attention to her departure. He had noticed it time and again during business hours when his lady clients slammed his office door so energetically that the woodwork partition that comprised two of the walls vibrated as if it were shaken by an earthquake. He filled his favourite pipe with some care and lay back in his armchair. "Looks as if we might have a quiet evening," he said. "I suppose you'll be doing a bit of writing?"

"Later on, perhaps," she replied. "First of all, I want to have a talk with you before Nick gets back."

"He hasn't been up to anything, has he? Seems to be a devil of a time finishing that picture."

"No, no; it's nothing to do with Nick. It's about this super-tax." Pleydell set down his pipe and leaned forward in his chair as Verity continued: "I can't think what the country is coming to, when a married woman can't earn a few pounds in her spare time. I've only spent the money on things I've been planning to buy for years; I'd no idea most of it would have to be paid to the tax people."

"Nobody would be any wiser about a few pounds," he replied. "The trouble starts when it runs into thousands and gets a lot of publicity into the bargain. And it won't end with this one payment. You'll write more books, I dare say; this may go on for years. Even if you stop earning big money, they'll keep pestering you to know why not."

"It's insufferable!" she protested. "Why don't people do something about such things?"

"Most people aren't a bit perturbed that the Government

should take fifteen shilling out of every pound you earn. If you put it to them, they'd only say you were lucky to earn that much, just as I've heard you talk about film stars' incomes before now."

"The whole thing is absolutely insidious!" exclaimed Verity, her indignation rising. "The laws ought to be changed. It's stifling freedom. I'll write an article about it. I'll start a campaign."

"I'm afraid you've left it a bit late," he shrugged. "In this country it takes a very long time to make a change of policy."

Verity was secretly furious that Pleydell accepted the whole business so philosophically and made no apparent attempt to do anything about it. He appeared to be far less indignant than she was; yet it was he who would have to do the actual paying. She had hoped to get him thoroughly worked up so that they could go into battle together like a couple of crusaders. But Pleydell had spent a lifetime trying to see the other man's point of view, and he did not get out of the habit very easily.

"I'll see Fitzpatrick next time I'm in Town," said Verity. "It's time he did something for us; I worked night and day during the election campaign."

Pleydell picked up his pipe and pressed down the tobacco firmly with his thumb, preparatory to lighting it. "My dear Verity, I don't suppose there's another woman in the whole of this constituency who will earn as much as you this year," he pointed out. "Fitzpatrick is far too busy getting a square deal for the thousands of poor people who are perpetually pestering him. Remember they represent thousands of votes."

"He's bound to consider my case. I'm a citizen; I have my rights."

"You have one solitary vote. I can't see that upsetting the Chancellor of the Exchequer very much when he plans the next Budget. There may be even a hundred thousand wealthy people who think the same as you do, but what are they among thirty million voters?" He struck a match and lit his pipe with great deliberation that drove his wife almost to screaming point.

"Why don't you *do* something?" she demanded. "We're not going to take this lying down, are we? We're not going to let ourselves be beaten down by a bunch of petty civil servants.

Try and concentrate, for goodness' sake! You've often told me about some of your customers boasting they never pay a penny income tax."

"And look what happens to them when they get found out! I happen to have my position to consider," he said reprovingly.

"Then stop considering it," she snapped. "I can always make enough money to keep the family now I've got a start."

He bit on his pipe and gave a little snort. "I like my work, and we're very comfortable here," he told her. "Why should we go taking ridiculous risks? We're not that sort of people."

Verity paced up and down the room. "I can't think why you accept things lying down like you do," she complained. "There are regulations that we have to fight against until they are repealed; and this is one of them. Why should a wife earning money be a burden to her husband? It simply doesn't make sense, and somebody's got to keep hammering at the Government until it penetrates their thick skulls."

He puffed out a cloud of smoke and slowly shook his head. "There are plenty of worse injustices to be found in the laws of this country," he told her. "But I don't intend to make a martyr of myself pointing them out to a bunch of political careerists whose only concern is their own advancement. You've got to be a realist about this, my dear."

"So you propose to pay up and look pleasant?"

"I don't see that there's anything else I *can* do. It will mean getting a mortgage on the house, I expect."

"But that's ridiculous!" she seethed. "Raising mortgages to pay taxes and then having to pay interest on the mortgage! It's idiotic, and doesn't make sense."

"There are a lot of things that don't make sense in this post-war world. I shall have to get the money somehow. Can't afford to have people talking."

"Who's going to talk?" challenged Verity. "Your friend, Wilkinson? I thought those people were sworn to secrecy."

"If we didn't find the money, they might even prosecute. At least, the bank would get to hear of it."

She leapt to her feet once more and looked down on him. "All right then," she declared, "we'll give them something to talk about and cut down the tax at the same time!"

"Verity, my dear . . . do keep calm," he begged, recoiling from the outburst.

"Keeping calm won't get us anywhere. You always want to adopt that policy of masterly inactivity. It won't pay the income tax demand. What we need is action, so do be quiet for a minute and listen to me!" It was obvious that she had to get into a towering rage before her idea would make any impression upon him, and she was rapidly approaching boiling-point now. "You keep telling me that this tax is so high because it comes on top of your own income," she began.

"That's right; it puts me well into the super-tax class."

She took a deep breath. "Supposing you and I were not married. If my income were treated separately, as if I were a spinster, how about that?"

"Well, you'd get a separate allowance——"

"And you wouldn't pay super-tax?"

"Of course not; but it's silly to talk like that."

She perched on the end of the settee and locked her hands over her right knee.

"Has it occurred to you that it might be possible to get a divorce before this tax falls due?" she demanded with tremendous intensity.

Pleydell caught his breath. "Get divorced?" he repeated, aghast. "Why the devil should we?" For a minute he did not take her seriously, nor even realize all the implications of the suggestion.

"To avoid paying thousands of pounds in super-tax," she replied, patiently as if to a child.

His pipe dropped from his fingers and he stared at her incredulously. "You must be mad," he said at last.

"I don't see why," she replied, trying to sound reasonable. "You're a business man; it should be perfectly clear to you as a sound financial proposition. For the past five years our marriage has been largely a matter of convenience. We've slept in separate rooms and more or less gone our own ways. I don't say that either of us has been technically unfaithful," she added hurriedly, "but we haven't exactly been passionately in love with each other."

Pleydell felt himself blushing around the back of his neck. "That sort of thing can't go on indefinitely," he said rather stiffly. "You know I'm very fond of you. I've let you have your own way in almost everything. The separate rooms, for instance, was your idea. You've been so busy with your various affairs these last few years that there seemed to be no time for any show of affection."

There's some truth in that, thought Verity, but showed no sign of weakening. "You have to admit we've rather grown away from each other in our interests," she argued. "You've stuck to your business and your local acquaintances. I've turned more towards the arts and the social services. It often happens with married couples and there's nothing much can be done about it. We've kept up appearances because it suited us in many ways. . . . There was Gillian for instance. She can take care of herself now, and in any case I've a feeling she'll soon be married."

He picked up his pipe and furtively smeared over some ashes on the carpet with his foot. "You don't seriously mean you want a divorce?" he said presently, when he could trust himself to speak.

"Have you any other way out of this difficulty to suggest?"

"This is no way out of it. I've told you we've simply got to pay up and make the best of it."

Verity shook her head decisively. She had the bit firmly between her teeth now, and he knew to his cost how tenacious she could be.

"In America we should most likely have been divorced years ago, and you may as well face the fact," she told him.

"I do not propose to conduct my life like a Hollywood film actor," he replied stiffly. "You don't appear to have given a thought to my position."

"Surely bank managers have been divorced before today," she argued.

"The bank would strongly disapprove. Clients would have no confidence in that type of man."

"What type of man?"

"The type who gets a divorce."

"But a man can't help it if he and his wife are incompatible."

"The bank, like the Church, would take the view that they should make an effort to adjust themselves to each other."

"How ridiculous! Anyway, you don't have to worry about the bank. You've a large enough private income to live on, and I can always help you out."

"Help me out?" he echoed in surprise. "How could you do that if we were divorced?"

She got off the arm of the settee and sat down in one corner of it. "Let's look at it sensibly," she urged. "There's no reason why we shouldn't go on living here together after the divorce has been made absolute. It has a lot of advantages. I doubt if either of us would want to marry again, and it would save breaking up this home and both of us making a new start."

He was too taken aback to speak for half a minute. "You really mean we should live under the same roof after we've been divorced?" he stammered.

"I don't see why not. It's been done before. After all, we are civilized people."

"But the bank would never——" he began to protest, when she interrupted.

"Will you forget about that bank of yours for a minute? This is purely a private matter. I keep telling you that you can well afford to be independent of them if they choose to get awkward."

Once again she could see the colour mounting the back of his neck. He got to his feet and stood looking down at her with a glare he usually reserved for recalcitrant junior clerks.

"You really have the most priceless nerve," he said slowly. "I've never come across anything quite like it. Ever since we were married, I've given way to you all along the line, mainly for the sake of peace and quiet. You had this house built entirely to suit you; you had only one child because you couldn't be bothered with any more; you've spent five evenings out of every seven at drama groups and lectures and committee meetings and literary circles. You've had a dozen boy friends dancing attendance at various times. And I have put up with everything for the sake of a reasonably peaceful family life. . . . But damn it all, there is a limit."

Verity lay back almost open-mouthed. She could not recall seeing Andrew on his high horse in this manner for years. For a moment she wondered if she had overstepped the mark, but she dismissed the idea at once. There must be no backing out now. She intended to see this scheme through with every ounce of drive she possessed. "If you feel as disgruntled as that, I should have thought you'd have welcomed a divorce," she snapped.

"You actually have the effrontery to think I'll give you a divorce?" he demanded.

"It's the least a gentleman can do."

"Then I'm no gentleman."

She shrugged. "In that case, I'll have to make some arrangements on my own account. Hassim Saroud has been pestering me for months to go away with him."

Pleydell looked as if he were about to explode. "You—you mean that—that——"

"That coloured gentleman," she replied evenly. "I wonder how your bank will react when they hear your wife has left you for the son of a sheik."

CHAPTER X

A MARRIAGE HAS BEEN DERANGED

"Time for bye-byes," yawned the blonde, going over to the mirror and running a comb through her curly hair. "It's been a lovely evening. I am enjoying this little trip."

Pleydell shuddered inwardly as if ice-cold razor blades were chasing round his stomach. He thought it had been a most unpleasant evening. He had hardly known what to say to this strange young woman, who had been introduced to him by a very discreet inquiry agent over cocktails in a chromium-plated bar in Jermyn Street.

If anyone had told him a month ago that he would be spending the night at the Beach Hotel, Redsea Bay, with a woman he had only met a few days previously, he would have done his best to knock the man down. Yet here he was, and, even more to the point, here was Miss Iris Digby-Leach.

The inquiry agent, to whom Verity's publisher, Paskin, had introduced him, had assured him that he would be quite safe in the experienced hands of Miss Digby-Leach, who was by way of being a professional co-respondent; indeed, the agent further assured Mr. Pleydell that he was lucky to get her.

"Just leave everything to Iris," were his instructions. "She knows exactly how these jobs are tied up." He had also suggested a suitable hotel at Brighton where the staff were presumably well versed in the routine of cutting matrimonial knots. But Pleydell had boggled at Brighton; it seemed both obvious and tawdry, and he had a feeling the judge might think the same.

At the Beach Hotel he had somewhat diffidently signed *Mr. and Mrs. Pleydell* in the register, the nquiry agent having duly booked a double room for him a few days previously.

Having had no previous experience of professional co-respondents, Pleydell did not know whether Miss Digby-Leach was merely fulfilling her professional duties when she informed him that she had taken a fancy to him. She told him he was reserved and gentlemanly—"not like some customers I've had to deal with". At the same time, she assured him that it wouldn't hurt him to appear a little more affectionate to-wards her in front of the hotel staff. "I've never been to this place before," she said, "and it doesn't do to take any chances. It would have been safer at Brighton, of course, but I like it better here. You've got very good taste."

Pleydell looked round the room. It was certainly com-fortable, with two small armchairs, a luxurious carpet, heavy curtains, strip lighting above the shining white wash basin and mirror, a loudspeaker in one corner and telephone at the bedside.

Miss Digby-Leach yawned again, placing her hand daintily before her skilfully made-up mouth. "I'll sleep this side if you don't mind," she murmured, moving her neat blue case to the end nearest the door and zipping it open. After a little fumbling she extracted a diaphanous black chiffon nightdress which she spread carefully on the bed. Then came an emerald green négligé, with slippers to match. "You like black nighties?" she inquired casually. "Most men do. I don't know why, but there's something about black . . ."

Pleydell swallowed hard and eventually found his voice. "I think you ought to understand, Miss Leach," he began.

"Oh, call me Iris," she urged, widening her appealing blue eyes. "You can't spend a night with a girl and call her Miss Leach."

"I'm trying to explain about that," he went on with a note of desperation. "I'm not proposing to spend the night . . . that is, I intend to doze in this armchair."

Iris flopped on the edge of the bed and eyed him incredulously. "You mean you're not coming to bed?" she demanded, as if she could not believe her ears.

Pleydell thrust his hands deep into his trouser pockets to conceal his embarrassment and began to pace up and down. "I thought I made it quite clear from the start that this was purely a business arrangement," he said in a hoarse voice which he hardly recognized as his own.

Iris tossed her fair curls. "That's what most of my clients say," she declared, "but when it gets to this time of night, most of them seem to want to change their minds. Of course, I knew all along you were different."

"How long have you been doing this?" he inquired, to distract her attention from himself.

"Over two years now. I used to be a shorthand-typist at the Investigation Bureau; that's how it all started."

"And you've finished with typing?"

She grinned. "The Bureau has to give me more for this trip than they'd pay for a month's hard work in the office. And quite right, too. Anybody can learn shorthand-typing, but this job is specialized. You have to know how to handle all sorts of men, and quite a lot about the divorce laws. And you have to learn when to talk and when to keep quiet. I tell you it's a line of its own."

She kicked off her high-heeled shoes and wriggled her toes beneath their gossamer nylon covering, stretching forth first one shapely leg and then the other as she did so.

"I'm sure you're very competent," he said nervously, "and I'm very anxious there should be no—er—unpleasantness. I appreciate that you have a job to do, and you're entitled to be treated with respect."

"Thank you," she replied evenly, and if there was a slight note of disappointment in her tone, it escaped him. "In that case, I'll go and undress in the bathroom."

She put on the green slippers with their elaborate gold bosses, picked up her nightdress and négligé and went into the adjoining bathroom, leaving the door a couple of inches ajar.

He slumped into one of the armchairs and stared at the electric fire. He had been a fool, he told himself, not to have taken a suite; then he could have spent the night on a sofa or settee in the sitting-room. And now he found himself in a situation so incredible that it was hard to believe he could ever have even contemplated it.

Here was he, Brewster Pleydell, a middle-aged bank manager, who had led an eminently respectable life, never looked at another woman since his marriage, faced with spending the night with a woman who was almost a complete stranger. And what seemed most fantastic of all, the woman who had been his wife for twenty years, and to whom he was still deeply attached, was entirely responsible for this paradoxical situation. And he was obeying her every whim like a fascinated rabbit, solely because she had decided that she wanted a divorce. His brain whirled madly as one absurdity after another chased crazily through it.

What would some of his highly respectable clients think if they saw him at this moment—Lady Wyckham, The Hon. George Tansley, Rupert Belvedere . . . ? Some of them had been reputed quite gay in their younger days, of course, but he was nearly fifty, and he ought to be serenely settled in life. It had been damnable of Verity to make him go through with this. He wished he could break her hold over him; it was like Svengali's in that old play he remembered seeing when he was a boy. She could even influence people whom she met for the first time, so what chance had you when you had been in love with her—still were in a way. . . .

He never knew whether she had really been bluffing about that coloured fellow, but he dared not let her make a fool of herself and of him too. Besides, he knew that when she was so fiercely intent upon anything as she was on this divorce, she would never rest until she had her way.

He sighed. Things might have been worse, he supposed. This Digby-Leach girl seemed a sensible little person, who was ready to treat this farce as a matter of routine.

At that moment the object of his thoughts came out of the bathroom wearing her green négligé over the black night-dress, and looking seductive enough to make even a middle-aged bank manager breathe a trifle harder. She could not have been more than twenty-seven, but without her sophisticated make-up her features had a childlike quality that her clients understandably found it difficult to resist.

But Pleydell was so ill at ease in this situation, the most

unorthodox he had encountered in his adult life, that he could
summon up no interest in Iris's sex appeal.

She placed her clothes, neatly folded, on a chair, and
slowly got into bed. It seemed to him that she was rather
turning the process into a ceremony, but he avoided meeting
her eyes and tried to talk casually.

"What time did you order tea for in the morning?" she
asked.

"Good heavens!" exclaimed Pleydell, who had forgotten
to do so in the stress of the evening's excitement.

"It's all right; I'll see to it," nodded Iris, picking up the
telephone and ordering morning tea for eight-thirty.

"I'm afraid that chair isn't going to be very comfortable,"
she said presently, when she had settled down in bed.

Pleydell had already discovered as much. "It's all right,"
he said. "I think I'll read for a while, if you don't mind the
light."

"Why not read to me? I love being read to."

"I hardly think you'll be interested in this book," he said,
taking the formidable-looking volume out of his case. He read
out the title. "*Principles and Theory of Joint Stock Banking.*"

"Well!" exclaimed Miss Digby-Leach. "What a book to
bring away for a gay week-end!"

He turned the pages, but found it difficult to concentrate.

"Tell me about your wife," said Iris suddenly, linking her
hands behind her head, a gesture which displayed her ample
figure. "Is she going off with another man?"

Pleydell cleared his throat. "No . . . er—nothing like that
as far as I know."

"Then why did she want to break up your marriage?"

"I'd really rather not discuss it."

He returned to his book and tried to lose himself in the
intricacies of bank balance sheets.

"I think she must be mad," declared Iris vehemently. "She
doesn't know when she's well off. Married to a man with a nice
home and a good, steady job. Let's see, what did you say your
business was?"

"I work in a bank," he said moodily.

"Just as I thought. Regular money and a good pension. I
don't know what some women want; I don't really."

"You gave up a steady job yourself," he reminded her.

"Steady, yes. But no money or prospects. A girl has to look out for herself."

"I quite agree," he nodded politely.

Miss Digby-Leach regarded him admiringly. "Fancy you being a big banking man," she murmured. The last banker I —er—acted for was a Mr. Prentice. You wouldn't know him, I suppose?"

Pleydell shook his head.

"He was a naughty old man, if you like," she recollected. "I had a real old time with him. He kept on insisting that if the judge was a Roman Catholic, he wouldn' believe the chambermaid's evidence unless she actually saw us . . . well, you know. . . ."

Mr. Pleydell was too embarrassed to inquire further into her experiences with the amorous Mr. Prentice, but she went on as if he were not there: "Yes, he'd got a way with him all right. I reckon he'd just about jump over the counter every time a woman under thirty came into the bank. I wasn't surprised his wife wanted a divorce; what he needed was one of those gland operations. I dare say he had a dozen lady friends his wife could have cited, but he didn't want them to be dragged into it . . . afraid of local scandal." She leaned forward and rearranged her pillow. "Thank goodness you're not that sort," she smiled. "It isn't often I get a good night's rest on these jobs. But I'm getting worried about you. Those chairs aren't made to spend the night in. You'll be as stiff as anything in the morning."

"I'll be all right," he assured her. "Would you like the light out now?"

"Not just yet."

He looked up and saw her smiling at him, her long, shapely white arms, bare to the shoulder, locked behind her curly blonde head.

"Tell me some more about your family," she suggested.

Rather to his surprise, he found himself telling this strange girl all about his married life, of his wife's forceful personality, of her talent as a speaker, writer and organizer, and of her success with *The Passionate Mirage*.

"So she wrote *that*, did she?" exclaimed Miss Digby-Leach, her eyes widening with interest.

"Have you read it?"

"Oh yes, everybody's reading it. I remember I had a good cry when I read the chapter where her husband gives her up." Her voice took on a sharper tone. "But that's no reason why she should expect you to do the same. Books are one thing; real life is a very different tin of peaches. D'you think she's got some other man in mind?"

He shrugged his shoulders. Naturally, he had not told her about the tax problem; in any case, he doubted if she would have understood it. "Of course, Verity's usually had one or two men friends around. She's a very attractive woman . . . always has been. At the moment, though, I think she just wants her freedom."

Even as he spoke the words, he wondered if they were strictly true. He had seen very little of his wife during the past few months. She could quite easily have met someone else. It might even be that sheik fellow. . . .

"Well, I think she's crazy," asserted Iris, noting his worried expression. "You're better without a woman like that. You're a decent, steady type; you should have a woman who values you. It's always the same though. Good men get rotters and worship 'em, while a really nice girl always falls for some rogue and lets him trample on her. It's a cockeyed world all right."

"Would you like a cigarette now?" he asked.

"I think I will. No, don't get up. I've some special ones of my own."

She got out of bed and went over to her case, which she opened and took out a cardboard box. "They're Turkish," she said, coming over to him. "How about trying one?"

She was standing beside him, and he was conscious of her unusual perfume and her body showing ivory beneath the filmy black nightdress.

"I—er—I think I'd better stick to my own," he said in answer to her question.

"Go on, try a Turkish," she urged. "That's your trouble you know. You ought to take a chance now and then; as it is, your wife's been having all the fun and you have been quite content to let her.

She leaned forward for him to light her cigarette. Her perfume seemed stronger than ever now; it was just a little overwhelming, he thought. Verity had always used it sparingly and had taught Gillian to do the same. Of course, one couldn't expect this young girl to display real taste in that direction, living the sort of life she did. Anyhow, the perfume was drowned almost immediately by the pungent aroma of the Turkish cigarette. She sat smoking it on the end of the bed while he lighted one for himself.

"Aren't you cold?" he asked solicitously.

"No, it's quite warm here in front of the fire."

She went on puffing away at the heavily scented cigarette, leaning forward occasionally to flick the ash into the ash-tray.

"I'm not quite sure what you ought to do about that wife of yours," she said presently. "Plenty of men would have put her across their knees and spanked her with a hairbrush. A man did that to me once," she added with a far-away look in her eyes.

"It wouldn't work with Verity," he assured her at once. "She'd walk right out of the house and never come back."

"Maybe that wouldn't have been such a bad thing," she observed. "It would have been a much cheaper way of getting a divorce. Still, if you'd done that, I should never have met you, and you are rather a pet. You're not the sort of man to strike his wife; I see that now."

"People in my position can't afford to do that sort of thing," he told her.

She expelled a stream of smoke, crossed her legs and said, "Are you sure you can afford *this* sort of thing?"

"I don't know," he replied wretchedly. "I expect it will cost me my job. I haven't been to see the staff manager at the bank yet. And I can't say I'm looking forward to it."

"But you are doing it simply because your wife insisted."

He had to admit that was true. For the past twenty years, when it came to the final show-down, he could not stand up to Verity. She overwhelmed him. It was rather like matching a flyweight boxer with a heavyweight. He simply collapsed before the tremendous force of her vitality.

"I begin to get some idea of the sort of woman she is," nodded Iris, stubbing out her cigarette and preparing to return to bed. "She should have had half a dozen kids to absorb her energy."

Yes, he thought, there's something in that. This girl was obviously no fool. She went across to the bed and returned with a spare pillow. "If you insist on spending the night in that chair, you may as well be as comfortable as possible," she said, arranging it behind him. "I know you won't get a wink of sleep," she added in a motherly tone. "Why don't you come to bed? We can put this pillow down the middle, or you can sleep between the blankets. . . ."

But Pleydell was obstinate and presently she climbed back into bed. "Now you listen to me for ten minutes," she said. "I know more about women than you do, and maybe I can give you a bit of useful advice."

He had no option but to listen, and presently found himself becoming quite interested as Iris began to enlarge upon the plan of campaign she suggested he should follow. It seemed to be worth trying at any rate. They talked until nearly one o'clock, and at last Iris said: "Well, think it over, and be sure to let me know how you get on. . . . Good night, old dear," she murmured sleepily——

She was asleep almost instantly. Pleydell settled in his armchair, the back of which was too short to rest the head comfortably. He tried sprawling his legs before him, but that was no more comfortable. He heard the clocks outside chime three, four, five and six, then dozed intermittently for about an hour. Iris awoke soon after eight and bade him undress and get into pyjamas.

Promptly at eight-thirty the chambermaid brought in their morning tea and pulled back the curtains, to reveal Iris lying in bed with one shapely arm around Pleydell's neck.

"Tea, darling," said Iris in honeyed accents, taking the tray from the maid and favouring him with a rather too obvious glance of affection. "Wake up, sleepyhead."

The chambermaid turned from the window and after one quick look, decided that her suspicions were correct. Wonder what his wife would say if she could see him, she reflected. Men of his age were always the worst. And as for that hussy . . . Oh, well, they'd paid their money the same as anybody else, and were entitled to room service.

Iris dropped two lumps of sugar into Pleydell's cup, then stirred it for him. "Come along, darling, drink up your nice cup of tea and then you won't feel so exhausted," she cooed. Pleydell took a sip and made a wry face. He hated sugar in his tea.

CHAPTER XI

GILLIAN TAKES THE PLUNGE

THE case of Pleydell *v.* Pleydell was undefended and presented few difficulties to the elderly judge who scuffled through the papers, asked a couple of curt questions and pronounced a decree. Luckily, the Press had not realized that the appellant was the famous lady novelist, so there were no photographers waiting outside the court when she came out with her solicitor, more than a little relieved to be out of the oppressive atmosphere. The spectacle of the slow-but-sure grinding of the English law had considerably depressed her and she took exception to the unctuous manner of the chambermaid when she gave evidence and described what she had seen in the hotel bedroom. Verity recalled the picture of the co-respondent, produced in evidence; she had seemed quite attractive and did not look more than twenty-five. She was still a little puzzled as to what exactly had happened on 'the night in question'. Surely Andrew hadn't felt really attracted towards that woman, the first time he had ever seen her?

During the few days after his return Andrew had resolutely refused to discuss the trip to Redsea Bay. When she tried to make a tentative inquiry, he had informed her rather stiffly that she would get her evidence, and he hoped she would be satisfied. She was herself a little surprised to find she was still curious to know about this girl; her novelist's imagination was already beginning to play with her as a possible character for her next book.

After saying good-bye to her solicitor, Verity called a taxi and went back to her flat in a turning off Sloane Square. There were only three rooms, but she had taken it, furnished, and it cost her £500 a year. She thought it exorbitant, but could find nothing cheaper in that exclusive corner of London. At least it was quiet, and she hoped she would be able to write there. So far, she seemed to have done very little but entertain people, most of whom were brought round for a glass of sherry by the indefatigable Mr. Paskin.

Dropping in for a sherry was perhaps Mr. Paskin's greatest

accomplishment as a publisher. He knew of the whereabouts of more sherry decanters and the nature of their contents than any of his rivals. Paskin certainly had a wide acquaintance in the literary world, but Verity found his friends too talkative. They invariably gave her a headache . . . or could it be the sherry?

She had thought that living on her own, without the cares of a fair-sized house, she would be able to work at least six hours a day and possibly more. But she discovered that London flat life, with the occasional assistance of a daily woman, can be far more time-wasting that she had ever imagined. She had, in fact, written only a couple of chapters of the new novel so far, and was not very satisfied with them. She put it down to the disturbance of her way of living for the past twenty years and to the upset caused by the divorce. She steadfastly refused to admit that she was emotionally distressed and discussed the business with Paskin as if she and Andrew were a couple of charac ers in a novel she was about to write.

Was she forcing herself to appear too detached about it all?

Perhaps the divorce was doing strange things to her sub-conscious mind; setting up queer little complexes and in-hibitions. She wished she hadn't talked so much to that psycho-analyst at that party in Pont Street last night.

She switched on the electric kettle to make some tea, and flopped heavily on the divan in the living-room. It was a warm summer afternoon and the flat seemed almost as airless as the court she had recently left. The day had been far more ex-hausting than she had expected. Her solicitor had assured her that it would be merely a routine case, but from the moment she left the flat in the morning she had had a feeling that some-thing would happen. It had kept her on edge all through the day. They were such a ghoulish crowd at the court, like carrion crows picking over the remains of mortified marriages. She thought that was rather a neat description, and made a note of it at the back of her diary, which she took from her bag, just in case she should ever want to describe a divorce court in a story.

The kettle boiled in the kitchen, and just as she was going in to make the tea the telephone rang in the hall. She picked up the receiver. "Oh, it's you, Nick. Just a minute, the kettle's boiling."

She put down the receiver and went to switch off the

kettle. It appeared that Nick had just regained possession of her portrait from an exhibition in Piccadilly where it had created a minor sensation, and he had been offered three hundred guineas for it—more than double the figure she had paid him. He wanted to know when he should return it. "Bring it round now; you'll be just in time for tea," she said, for he lived only a few hundred yards away.

He said he must do a little shopping first.

She went into the kitchen and started laying a tray. It really was a dreadful bore preparing meals; she must make a definite effort to get a full-time maid, even if it cost her five pounds a week. She really hadn't the time to cope with all the domestic chores, particularly if there was entertaining to be done.

When the doorbell rang before she had taken the tea into the living-room, she thought at first that Nick had abandoned his shopping expedition. So she was somewhat surprised to see Gillian standing there, very stylishly dressed and looking very much at her ease.

"Why didn't you 'phone me?" asked Verity, leading the way into the living-room.

"I tried twice yesterday afternoon, but the line was engaged, and last night there was no reply."

"There's nothing wrong, is there?" asked Verity.

"Nothing at all, except that I appear to be a sort of orphan," said Gillian, settling herself on the settee. "I was in court, but you had your back to me."

Verity paused in the act of pouring tea. "You came up by yourself?" she asked.

"Seeing one's parents divorced after twenty years of married life seemed to me to be an experience I could not afford to miss," replied Gillian pleasantly. "Though, of course, it was very disappointing. Didn't you think so?"

"I was thankful it went through so quickly," admitted Verity, passing her a plate of bread-and-butter.

They ate and drank in silence for a little while, then Verity inquired if Erika was looking after the house efficiently.

Gillian nodded. "And Daddy's still going to the bank, though he says he doesn't know how much longer they'll let him carry on. He has to come up to Head Office next week for a special interview with all the chiefs. He doesn't say much, but I think he's dreading it."

"Oh, nonsense!" said her mother. "What can they possibly do to him? It isn't a crime to get divorced."

"It seems it's one of the things that are not done in the bank. They appear to look upon it as an offence rather like issuing forged cheques. At least, that's the impression I get."

"Well, if they're out to make trouble, I'll go round and see the joint general manager, or whoever it is, myself," said Verity. "If I take a far greater risk of unpleasant publicity upsetting my public, I don't see why the bank shouldn't take a chance with a man who's served them faithfully for a quarter of a century."

"You know what bank people are," shrugged Gillian. "They probably look on Daddy as Casanova and Errol Flynn rolled into one, and think he's got half a dozen blondes locked away in the strong-room."

"I wish you'd let me know when you hear anything," said Verity.

Gillian, who had begun by reserving all her sympathies for her father, now could not help feeling rather sorry for her mother. It was her fault of course, but she was going to be sorry for upsetting a comfortable married life that had been nearing its silver wedding anniversary. She would discover that she was not so self-sufficient as she had imagined, and that life on one's own could be very lonely. All the same, she was lucky having this marvellous flat in an artistic neighbourhood. Gillian certainly envied her that.

"Of course, I'll let you know," she nodded in response to her mother's request.

"Your father is inclined to let people bully him," went on Verity as if to justify herself. "He has done a lot of good work for the bank, and they ought to treat him properly. If they don't, they'll lose my account for a start, and probably several more, and I shall take the first opportunity of telling them so."

"I wouldn't do that, unless Daddy makes a definite complaint," put in Gillian hastily. "He likes to think he's capable of conducting his own affairs in the bank."

"I won't be able to see him until the decree is made absolute, so I must rely on you to keep us in touch," said Verity. "And by the way, you can spend a day or two here whenever you like."

She's lonely already, thought Gillian.

Possibly because of their recent separation, or perhaps because of Verity's trying day, mother and daughter were chatting on more intimate terms than they had been for a long time when Nick arrived, carrying the portrait heavily swathed in corrugated cardboard.

He did not seem unduly surprised to see Gillian, and greeted her quite casually. Her response was so offhand that Verity was patently surprised. "I've had an inquiry from the Municipal Gallery in Liverpool; they're holding a portrait exhibition in September, and they'd like to have it," he said as he handed over the picture. "What do you think?"

"Certainly," nodded Verity, always on the alert for any publicity of the right sort. "My new book ought to be out by then."

He settled in an armchair and accepted a cup of tea. Gillian thought he looked paler than when he had been staying with them at Firbright. The skin on his face seemed flabbier and his mouth had a hard line.

"By the way, isn't the divorce due about now?" he inquired somewhat diffidently.

"It was today," replied Verity. "And that reminds me, I'll have to write one or two letters in connection with it before the post goes. Would you excuse me for ten minutes? Gillian, see that Nick has some more tea...."

She went off to the bedroom where she kept her small escritoire.

"What are you doing up here?" inquired Nick rather listlessly.

Gillian hesitated a moment, then said with sudden decision, "As a matter of fact, I came up to look at some rings—engagement rings."

"Indeed? Congratulations." His voice showed little sign of any sort of emotion.

"Are you surprised?"

"No, of course not. You know I've always thought you very attractive."

"Thank you," she replied somewhat pr'mly. "You've developed a gift for saying the right thing."

He smiled wearily. "I think I acquired it at Firbright . . . or rather I learned to say it at the right time while I was there. Did you find the ring you wanted?"

"I found lots. It's rather difficult to choose."

"I dare say Harold will be ready to help. It is Harold, isn't it?"

She nodded.

"I'm sure you'll be riotously happy. It's time you flew from the nest, I think."

"You mean there soon won't be any nest left?"

"Doesn't it rather look like that?"

"But I don't intend to leave Daddy," she told him. "We'll either go and live with him, or he'll come to us. I insisted on that."

Nick leaned forward in his chair and seemed to come to life. "I was all in favour of your getting married," he said, "but if you're only doing it to find your father a home, I'm not so sure it'll work out."

"Don't be silly, Nick. That isn't the only reason. In any case, I think I'm old enough to know my own mind."

"Certainly," he agreed. "Sorry if I sounded like an interfering Aunt Fanny. It's really no business of mine."

He was lying back in his chair with his eyes half-closed.

"Don't you feel well, Nick?" she asked.

"I was out late at a party last night. Must have mixed my drinks. When's the wedding going to be?"

"Not for quite a while. Might be a year."

"Will you send me an invitation?"

"Do you want to come?"

He opened his eyes and seemed to look right through her. "You'll be a wonderful bride," he said distantly. "Yes, I think I'd like to be there. It would be fun to design you a nice, virginal head-dress for a wedding present."

"Have you heard from your wife?" asked Gillian in a tone that she hoped was suitably remote.

"Good lord, no. I don't expect to. Are you trying to put a damper on this cosy little conversation?"

"Not at all. It was you who were sounding bored."

"I'm terribly sorry. Perhaps I'll feel better if you give me another cup of tea."

She refilled his cup for him.

"Well, your friend Harold deserves a little encouragement," he said presently. "And I'm sure he'll appreciate his good luck for many a long year."

"We intend to be riotously happy," announced Gillian

defiantly, "and I shall have a large family—at least three boys and a girl."

"That'll help to take your mind off the sad state of the world at large," smiled Nick a trifle wistfully. "I take it the divorce didn't make any difference to Harold's enthusiasm then?"

Gillian smiled. "That's what rather brought things to a head. He was so nice about it. One or two of our friends have gone very upstage, but Harold was a pet—he comes round and keeps Daddy company at week-ends, and sometimes in an evening, and he's run errands and witnessed documents and done all sorts of odd jobs to help me when Erika's been out."

"So you decided he's too good to miss," smiled Nick. "And I don't blame you. Men like that are rare birds these days. I doubt if there are five in the whole of Chelsea!"

"What have you been doing since you got back?"

"Mostly housework. A daily char is almost worth her weight in uranium these days."

"Have you done any more portraits?"

"There's some talk about the picture of World Citizen Number One, but nothing definite."

Gillian poured herself some more tea and glanced at him from time to time when she thought he was not looking at her. He seemed nervy and a trifle restless, his long, sensitive fingers were never still, and his hair flopped down over his right eye from time to time, to be pushed back with an abrupt gesture. He seemed to have lost much of that detached air of repose which he acquired during his stay in Firbright. She wondered vaguely if he were unhappy. . . . Perhaps some other woman had come along and upset him?

Then Verity returned to the room and cut short her speculations. She found herself hoping he said nothing to her mother about her engagement, and rather to her surprise he made no reference to it.

When he had gone, Gillian helped her mother to wash up the tea-things. She realized now that she would say nothing about Harold to her yet. She had formed the habit of never telling her of any plan, however mature, for Verity had a knack of upsetting it. Of course, she could not possibly break the engagement; there was no reason at all why she should want to. But Gillian was taking no chances.

CHAPTER XII

PLEYDELL ON THE CARPET

IT WAS not the first time Andrew Brewster Pleydell had
visited the head office of the Central Bank. In fact, most
branch managers were called to that palatial building about
once every two years, sometimes more often if there was a
question of a bad debt to be thrashed out.

Like almost every other manager, he rarely enjoyed the
trip. One could never be quite sure what surprise they would
spring in those lavishly furnished offices, with their huge desks,
thick pile carpets and batteries of telephones. At Firbright he
was the captain of his own little barque: here he was constantly
reminded that it was only a very small vessel in an enormous
fleet.

As usual on these occasions, he arrived early in town
and visited a large men's hairdresser's near Liverpool
Street Station, where he had a haircut, shampoo and face
massage. It cost him eight-and-sixpence altogether, but he
always felt it was worth it when there was an ordeal to be
faced.

And this time it was no ordinary ordeal, a mere question of
settling some client's affairs. On this visit his whole future
was at stake.

He walked slowly in the direction of Fenchurch Street,
where the head office was situated, feeling none too sure of
himself despite the invigorating effects of the facial. He tried
to reassure himself that, unlike thousands of his colleagues, he
was not dependent entirely upon the bank for a living. If the
worst came to the worst, he could live on his private income
without any hardship.

However, that was not much consolation. Banking was his
life; he knew of no other way of passing his time, apart from
playing golf and running around in the car. He could hardly
bring himself to contemplate the vacuum in his life if he did not
leave for the bank promptly at nine every morning.

A clock on a large building told him he had still ten
minutes to spare, and he lingered before a series of shabby

little shops which always seemed to be in the midst of a sensational sale 'owing to the expiration of lease'.

He could not imagine what life would be like if he could not spend several hours a day in the familiar surroundings of the manager's room at Firbright. He was accustomed to shouldering an important responsibility; it was unfair to deprive him of that privilege. Time enough to have to face a contingency like that when he had to retire at sixty and make way for a younger man. Just now he was in his prime and right on top of his work. There was not a man in the bank better suited to his particular job. Not that the bank would ever admit it. They thought of their staff in terms of units.

He arrived at the elaborate portico with four minutes to spare, and decided he might as well go in. The huge banking hall, with its tessellated floors and enormous fountain playing in the centre, never failed to overawe him slightly. This was the heart of the machine he worked for. Or would it be better described as the brain, which constantly sent out its messages to its two thousand nerve centres, which accordingly called in or extended their overdrafts, depending on the state of the money market?

Crossing over to the lifts, he entered one and was taken to the fourth floor, where he made his way along a maze of corridors. The place was like a town; over two thousand clerks worked under this roof, which housed the clearing departments employing several hundred girl clerks.

At length he found the office of the Home Counties staff superintendent, and was shown into an austerely furnished waiting-room which faced a white glazed brick wall of another wing of the building. There was another man waiting already, a sandy-haired, middle-aged man who was pacing up and down nervously, looking at his watch from time to time. Pleydell politely wished him 'good morning' and picked up a copy of the *Financial News* from a side table. From time to time he cast a pitying glance at the sandy-haired man. The old tactics, he thought. They had probably kept the poor devil waiting an hour already. He was in a terrible state of nerves, and they would have him just where they wanted him.

Pleydell recollected one of the divisional superintendents telling him that all the big banks averaged a case of embezzlement apiece every day, which meant that somebody was always on the carpet. The man pacing up and down nervously twisted the ends of his little sandy moustache, then took out a handkerchief and wiped his damp palms. Pleydell read down a list of Stock Exchange quotations with meticulous care, though their significance entirely escaped him. He wondered how much the other man had taken, and studied him curiously.

During his banking career Pleydell had never encountered a colleague who had appropriated the bank's money, though he had heard of many cases at secondhand. As for himself, he was always quite scrupulous in this direction. He never charged a penny more than his expenses when he was on any outside work, though he could have passed double or treble the amount without any query.

He had sometimes wondered if he were desperately hard up whether he would have dipped his hand into the till. You were in perpetual fear of being found out, of course, and the theft would certainly be discovered in the long run unless you managed to replace the money. He imagined that ninety per cent of the embezzlers hoped to do that, but as a rule they only sank deeper into the mire. A lot of them were not really bad, he thought. Given another chance, they would probably go dead straight. But the bank never gave them a second chance. Indeed, they were told to consider themselves lucky to be allowed to refund the money and escape prosecution.

If they were not in a position to find the money, and if it was a very large sum, then the bank did indeed prosecute, and a prison sentence of two years or more was invariably the result. But if the sum was comparatively small it was considered sufficient to deprive the clerk of his living. In any case, the bank was insured against such defalcations; every clerk paid premiums during his first five years in their employ.

Yes, there was undoubtedly a shifty look about the other man, Pleydell decided. His eyes were set rather too closely together and he had a mean expression when you caught him half-face to the light. A man of that type should never have been accepted for the bank in the first place, he reflected. Whoever interviewed him had been sadly lacking in an elementary sense of judgement of human types.

The sandy-haired man sat down at last, and there was no sound in the waiting-room save the rustle of Pleydell's paper, occasional footsteps in the corridor outside and the distant rattle of typewriters and electric accounting machines. Their existence seemed to have been forgotten. Pleydell told himself that it was all part of the technique; they weren't as busy as all that, but merely putting on an act. The main thing was not to allow oneself to get rattled, to keep in mind that you were just another item in their daily routine.

Obviously the sandy-haired man had not realized this; or else his conscience was upsetting his composure. He wriggled uncomfortably in his seat, ran his finger round the edge of his collar, nervously straightened his tie for the tenth time, then cleared his throat with a series of tiny coughs. Finally he moistened his lips and said, "I—er—I suppose they don't allow smoking in here?"

Pleydell lowered his newspaper and looked across at him. "I don't know of any law against it," he replied in a non-committal tone.

The sandy-haired man took a silver cigarette-case from his pocket and opened it. Then he hesitated and, after an appreciable pause, snapped it shut.

What's he got to lose, thought Pleydell, feeling sorrier for him than ever. Whatever their decision is, it's already made, and a cigarette can't influence it very much one way or the other.

Looking at his wrist-watch, the sandy-haired man went on: "Do they always keep people waiting? I've been here over an hour."

"It all depends," replied Pleydell guardedly. "There's no point in worrying about it, anyhow. They take their own time. After all, they're paying us, I suppose."

The other nodded gloomily. "Yes, that's one way of looking at it," he agreed. "All the same, I like to get these things over and done with. I never could stand waiting around. Have you been here before?"

"Oh yes, several times," Pleydell told him. "There's nothing to worry about, really. Once you get inside, you find they are quite human."

"I wish I could believe that," said the other almost under his breath, taking out his handkerchief again. "I expect you're used to this, but it's all new to me. And I can't say I like it very much. This place is too big; it gets you down. I've always worked in a small branch with a friendly sort of atmosphere. This is worse than a munition factory.

Pleydell studied him with rather more interest. He was a comparatively young man in the early thirties with a slightly mottled complexion and red hands that appeared to protrude a couple of inches too much from the sleeves of his black coat. Pleydell had a picture of his anxious wife at home, apprehensively awaiting her husband's return, and wondering what the future could hold for them now, whether they would have to give up their neat villa and withdraw the children from their private school.

The sandy-haired man coughed apologetically and said, "Do you happen to know anything about Hertfordshire, by any chance?"

"I've worked there all my life. Do you come from——?"

"No, no; I'm in for a job there."

"In for a job!" echoed Pleydell, his images of the embezzler fading like a spendthrift's legacy.

"Yes, it's a managership . . . quite a step up for me. I'm chief clerk at Dagenham; been there four years."

Pleydell could not have imagined a less suitable type for a managerial position. A man like this could not even begin to talk to an important client. However, he did his best to display a polite interest in the other's good fortune.

"You're quite young for a manager's job," he said mildly. "I suppose they are starting you off at a small branch."

"I'm not sure if I've got the job yet. I think there are one or two more in for it. And it isn't such a small branch either. It's a place called Firbright. D'you happen to know it at all?"

Pleydell caught his breath, but before he could say anything the door opened and a honey-blonde in a mauve overall smiled at him and murmured, "Mr. Tapper will see you now, Mr. Pleydell."

.   .   .   .

Pleydell was seething with indignation when he took the visitor's chair in the roomy office of Mr. Felix Tapper, the Home Counties section staff superintendent. In fact, he would have been very tempted to use some extremely forcible language but for the fact that Mr. Tapper had taken the wise precaution of having his mauve-clad secretary work in the same room.

This always seemed to Pleydell an underhand sort of thing to do, but he knew from experience that it was the customary practice of staff supervisors. Maybe it saved them some unpleasant scenes; it also provided them with a witness who could be very useful upon occasion.

Mr. Tapper, however, was adept at avoiding scenes by the ready use of his glib tongue. In fact, Mr. Tapper enjoyed talking. He had argued himself into his present position and would, no doubt, verbally insinuate himself into an even better one during the next few years. Like the most polished of patter comedians, he needed only the semblance of a cue to send him into one of his numerous routines.

He was a dark, well-groomed man of about thirty-five, with piercing brown eyes and a prominent cleft chin. His suits were expensive and his nails obviously professionally manicured. Pleydell had never had much time for Mr. Tapper, for in his experience, the staff superintendent was always more interested in playing up to his own immediate superiors than in rendering assistance to branch managers who were short of staff.

On this occasion Pleydell did not intend to waste any time with Mr. Tapper. When he could speak with reasonable restraint, he said, "Would you ask your typist to telephone Sir Herbert and tell him I must see him?" Sir Herbert Simcox was the general manager in charge of the Home Counties section.

"I'm afraid that's out of the question. I happen to know Sir Herbert is very busy this morning. He has given me full authority to settle this matter."

"So he may have done," snapped Pleydell, "but I don't happen to approve of the way you're going about it. I'm entitled to see Sir Herbert, and I intend to see him if I have to wait all day."

Pleydell noticed Tapper shoot a meaning glance at his secretary, who was obviously following the conversation very closely, before asking, "May I ask what you don't approve of?"

"If you will send your girl out of the room, I'll tell you in pretty strong language," retorted Pleydell. The secretary looked hard at her typewriter keyboard, but made no move.

"I've served this bank for twenty-eight years, and I'm entitled to a square deal," continued Pleydell.

"If you'll only tell me what's upsetting you——" began Tapper, but Pleydell interrupted:

"I'll make my complaints to Sir Herbert, if you don't mind."

It was slowly beginning to dawn upon Tapper that his visitor was in a rare and almost uncontrollable rage which was likely to defy even his smooth-tongued persuasion, so he immediately slipped into his special line of admonitory reproof reserved for clerks who were proving obstinate.

"I must say I'm surprised at your taking this line, Mr. Pleydell, when I'm only trying to help. This case of yours has caused quite a lot of unfavourable comment, and you know how the bank feels about things like that."

"As I've been in the bank ten years longer than you have, Tapper, I think I've an idea how it feels about most things. When I was appointed to my present job, I was interviewed by Sir Herbert, and all I'm asking is that I see him before I leave it, so that I can explain the full circumstances of my case."

"You can rely on me to let Sir Herbert know——"

"This happens to be a strictly private matter that I prefer not to trust to a third party," replied Pleydell. "Or parties," he added, with a meaning glance in the direction of the blonde in the corner.

Tapper was about to register a further protest, but he was forestalled by the door opening suddenly. He looked round quickly.

"Why, Sir Herbert . . ." he began.

"I'm free now any time you can come in," said Sir Herbert.

Pleydell rose. "I would very much like to have a word with you, Sir Herbert, if you could spare ten minutes," he said.

Sir Herbert came into the room. "Why, it's Pleydell," he murmured.

"It's vitally important to me, Sir Herbert, or I wouldn't trouble you," persisted Pleydell.

Sir Herbert pursed his lips for a moment. He had just admitted he was not engaged, so he could not very well retract.

"All right, Pleydell," he said at last. "Come into my room."

Pleydell could not resist a triumphant glance in the direction
of the staff superintendent before closing the door behind him
and following the general manager along the corridor to an
office which was considerably larger than the entire floor
space of some of the smaller branches of the Central Bank.

Sir Herbert nodded to Pleydell to take a chair, and sat
down at his desk. He was a big man, approaching sixty, with
heavy jowls, friendly grey eyes and a humorous mouth. He
owed his rise in the bank to the fact that he had married the
daughter of one of its most influential directors, but he had
brought a certain amount of sympathetic understanding to his
work, and had probably done his job better than any of his
fellow general managers.

He passed over a box of cigarettes.

"Well, Pleydell, I must say I can't understand this business," he began. "It isn't like you at all. I always had the idea
you were very happy domestically."

Pleydell hesitated. He could hardly tell Sir Herbert that
the divorce was a put-up job, nor could he go into all the
details of his 'guilt' in the matter.

"Perhaps I ought to explain, sir, that my wife is a very
unusual type of woman," he said cautiously.

"Ah, yes, she's written a book or something, hasn't she?"

"That's right, sir. It's had a lot of publicity, and I think
it—well, it had an unsettling effect on her."

"You mean she's gone running after a younger man?"

Pleydell straightened himself in his chair and replied
rather stiffly, "No, sir, not to my knowledge."

"Then you really are the guilty party in this divorce?"

"I suppose you would describe it as technically guilty,"
admitted Pleydell. "But I've no intention of living with, or
marrying, anyone else. In fact, there isn't anybody."

Sir Herbert rubbed his fleshy chin thoughtfully. "This
seems to be a very remarkable business, Pleydell. I must
confess I don't quite understand it."

Pleydell launched upon what he hoped was a plausible
account of Verity wanting her freedom to embark upon an
independent life of her own, to devote herself to art, to shake
off the domestic routine that had been curtailing her artistic
development.

They talked for more than half an hour. Sir Herbert

H

offered some friendly advice, to which Pleydell listened respectfully. Indeed, taken all round, Sir Herbert seemed to be enjoying himself immensely; he rather fancied himself in the position of father confessor to the three thousand clerks directly under his control. It made a pleasant change from overdrafts and balance sheets.

When he judged Sir Herbert was in a sufficiently mellow mood, Pleydell assumed the rôle of the trusted employee with a grievance, and strengthened his case immediately by stating that he had only heard of his removal from Firbright when he was told by a candidate for his job. This certainly scored a point, for he saw Sir Herbert make a note on his pad, and he hoped that Mr. Tapper would himself be brought on to the carpet in the near future.

For once in a way, Pleydell felt genuinely inspired as he outlined his case. He mentioned all the improvements he had brought about since he went to Firbright, how the staff had nearly doubled, and the profits increased over eighty per-cent. There had never been a serious complaint from a customer, nor any staff difficulties. With a suspicion of a catch in his voice, Pleydell added that he had hoped to end his banking days there, that he had no ambition towards a larger branch and bigger salary.

Sir Herbert nodded his head sympathetically from time to time. There was no plea that appealed to himself as much as one of complete devotion to the mighty Central Bank and its long-established traditions. He drew little designs on his blotter and frowned thoughtfully until his bushy eyebrows almost seemed to meet.

When Pleydell had finished, Sir Herbert sat looking out of the window without speaking for some seconds. Then he swung round in his chair. "It seems to me that this is a case in which the board might make an exception," he said at last. "I'll have a chat with Lord Eltham and one or two of the directors, but I can't make any promises. There's just a chance they might agree to break the precedent."

He flung down his pencil and looked across at his visitor.

"You'd better go and have some lunch, Pleydell," he nodded. "Nothing like a good meal to put you right when your nerves are a bit on edge. Try the North Ludgate Hotel and tell the head waiter I sent you."

CHAPTER XIII

OUT OF CHARACTER

WHEN Verity heard from Gillian that Pleydell had resigned from the bank, she experienced a vague twinge of regret, for she knew what his job had meant to him and wondered how he could possibly spend his time. Her brain had already begun to busy itself with possible solutions to the problem: he could act as her manager, look after her accounts and perhaps check up some of the facts in the new book she was writing. But before she had an opportunity to put her thoughts into words, Gillian said:

"He seems to be frightfully busy, what with one thing and another. I do wish you'd come down one day and see if you can't have a talk with him. He's doing the most peculiar things. . . ."

"Such as what?"

"Well, he's taking a course of tapestry work."

"Tapestry work?" echoed Verity in a voice that rose slightly above normal pitch.

"Yes, you know; he has one of those funny old frames and sits for hours with his patterns and threads. He says it's good for his nerves."

"But he never had the slightest inclination for that sort of thing," murmured Verity with a puzzled frown.

"He says it must have been latent inside him."

"Rubbish!" snapped Verity, who resented any encroachment upon her monopoly of artistic talent in the family.

"But that isn't all by a long way," persisted Gillian, with a certain satisfaction at her mother's discomfort. "He's started wearing the most awful clothes—open-necked shirts in peculiar shades of orange and green, and old flannel trousers and sandals."

Verity began to look alarmed.

"You don't think this business has sent him a bit—er——"

"I don't know what to think," replied Gillian. "Yesterday, for instance, he said he had decided to take up water colours, and he was going to the art school right away. Imagine him . . . in the midst of all those bits of girls!"

"But he's got no idea of art," said Verity. "He never knew a Matisse from a Hogarth."

"He says he'll bring a completely fresh mind to it. And he's toying with the idea of doing sculpture as well."

Verity frowned. "Does he seem rational in his general behaviour?" she asked.

"He doesn't stand on his head or anything like that, but I wouldn't be a bit surprised to find he's taken up Yogi when I get back. He keeps saying a new world is opening up before him, and he's advancing towards fresh horizons. Oh dear, I hope he won't turn poetical," she added fearfully.

Verity leaned back in her comfortable armchair and pondered upon this new development. It was a little hard, she thought, when she was in the midst of the highly complicated plot of her new novel, to have disturbing real-life situations thrust upon her.

"How long has he been like this?" she demanded presently.

"Since the first day he left the bank. He keeps saying he has embarked upon a new spiritual phase of his life."

Verity knitted her brows. "I don't like the sound of it at all," she said. "I'd no idea he'd turn cranky at his age. I wonder if it would be any use taking him to a good psychiatrist."

"I doubt it," said Gillian. "Anyhow, he's reasonably harmless at the moment. Psycho-analysing him might release a few more inhibitions we haven't bargained for."

"It's very worrying," said her mother, "and I can't very well help you just yet. The decree isn't absolute until next month, and we aren't supposed to see each other at all until that's all settled." She hesitated a moment, then went on to ask: "You're quite sure it isn't some woman who's influencing him to dabble in these arts and crafts? He used to talk quite a lot to that awful Higham-Wickes creature who runs the antique shop."

Gillian shook her head quite definitely. "He doesn't seem a bit interested in women; as far as I can see, he's completely immersed in this art nonsense."

"But he can't be taking it seriously," protested Verity. "I

mean, surely he doesn't think he can make a living from art."

"He says he doesn't have to worry about that any more. When I'm married, he says he'll have enough for his simple wants. Oh, I forgot to mention he's getting keen on cookery, too. He insists that he'll be able to do most things for himself. Says he wants to be independent of all women."

Verity took a cigarette from a box on the side table and lighted it. She had been smoking a lot more during the past few weeks; for one thing her new book had been going none too well, and an hitherto occasional cigarette had become almost a chain, for they took the edge off her nerviness. It also happened that she had received a box of five hundred free in addition to her fee of fifty guineas for endorsing an advertisement for a new brand of cigarette. They were a little hot to the palate, but she felt she ought not to give them all away.

"You don't think this cooking craze is an excuse to go into the kitchen and hang around Erika?" she suggested.

"At least, that would be normal," replied Gillian. "And Erika is quite capable of looking after herself; she's handed off far too many G.I.s in her time to let a middle-aged bank manager worry her."

"I dare say," said Verity. "But she might get ideas that he's really serious. She's the sly type, you know; the sort that get their men to marry them on the quiet and then present the family with a *fait accompli*."

"I don't think you need worry. Erika is far too interested in young men. Several times lately I've seen her on the back of a motor-bike; I think the young man is an operator at one of the cinemas."

"Well, don't leave her alone with your father any more than you can help," adjured Verity. "And I'll try and think of some way to get him out of this arty-crafty phase."

"Why don't you ring him up and have a serious talk? The King's Proctor could hardly raise any objection."

Verity considered this for a moment or two, then shook her head. "It would be better for me to see him," she decided. "He's very clever at wriggling out of things on the telephone; I suppose he picked that up at the bank. And I must push on with my book; Paskin keeps worrying me to finish it in time for the autumn lists. I simply can't concentrate on developing a story when I've got family worries on my mind. While I think of it, I suppose everything's going smoothly between you and Harold?"

"Oh yes; we've almost decided on the first or second week in June for the wedding."

Verity nodded approvingly. "Thank goodness something is running to schedule," she murmured. "You can be married from here—at least we'd have the reception at Sloane Mansions Hotel, but the Parish Church would be lovely for the wedding."

"I'd never thought of that," replied Gillian, who had taken it for granted that she would be married in Firbright.

"I don't think I want a grand wedding," she said nervously. "So many of them seem to be followed by a divorce in next to no time. Besides, it's so expensive. . . ."

"I shall look after that," her mother promised her. "After all, we have our position to consider."

She means *she* has a position, thought Gillian. And she pictures herself as dominating the whole proceedings. Well, for once in a way I'll push her nose out of joint. If a bride can't be the centre of attraction at a big wedding, then she hasn't much hope for the future.

"I'll talk to Harold about it," she said presently. "Have you seen anything of Nick lately?"

Verity shook her head. "I think he's away in the provinces, painting some local bigwig's picture. Last time I saw him he said he was so hard up that he expected that he'd be reduced to painting aldermen. I wish he'd come round here; I'd like to discuss your father with him, Nick's a man of the world—it's quite likely he would be able to suggest some solution to the difficulty."

"It will probably solve itself in time," said Gillian. "I suppose Nick never mentions his wife. . . ."

"Good heavens, no! I'd forgotten he had one. Now I come to think of it, he did tell me he was married. It hasn't worked out, of course; it rarely does with artistic people."

She sighed, just a shade too dramatically, Gillian thought.

"That's why I'm glad you're marrying a boy in a good, steady job," pursued Verity. "It's a much safer proposition if you want the marriage to last. I don't suppose either of you will do anything spectacular in art or science or public affairs, but you'll be much happier in your own little niche. . . ."

Again she sighed, as if to convey her sacrifice of private

happiness to the cause of art and her devoted public. Gillian was not impressed. In some moods she rather resented the manner in which they had almost thrust her into Harold's arms, as if he were the last hope of a fading old maid; then, after reading the divorce cases in the newspapers, and hearing of her acquaintances' own unhappy marital experiences, she felt relieved that she had met someone as trustworthy and devoted as Harold. There had been times when she found him slightly boring, but he would never prevent her from living her own life, a privilege granted to few people in a mass-production world.

She suddenly came out of her reverie to realize that her mother was talking again.

"I don't know what to do about Andrew," she was saying. "Of course, I realize that he's no longer my responsibility, but after all, we were married for more than twenty years, and I wouldn't like to think I was the cause of his—er—deteriorating. She lighted yet another cigarette.

.   .   .   .   .

If Andrew Brewster Pleydell was not exactly enjoying his new freedom, he was far less bored than he had expected. His general manager had given him a lot of advice about starting afresh and getting right away from the old life, and he was doing his best to follow it. The worst time was when he woke in the morning and realized that there was no hurry to get up and dash off to the bank. He overcame this usually by imagining that it was Saturday or Sunday.

For the first two or three weeks he had spent most of his time acquiring his outlandish new wardrobe and the various accessories of the hobbies he proposed to pursue. Avoiding the familiar faces of his Firbright shopkeeper clients, he went to St. Albans, where he haunted those peculiar little shops which abound in cathedral towns to cater for the artistically minded.

After a few not very successful attempts at tapestry work, however, he decided to graduate in something rather less complicated, and turned to rug-making. He argued that even if a rug were not a success from the point of design, it could always fulfil a useful purpose in the spare bedroom or possibly beneath the kitchen sink.

Rug-making he found comparatively simple and quite absorbing, even though it made his fingers sore at first. The designs were reasonably easy to follow and the results encouraging after two or three hours' work. There was something soothing about the regular prodding and pulling that calmed his nerves and kept his mind pleasantly occupied.

Cooking, too, he found, had its fascination. He would spend hours in the kitchen when Erika was out. First of all he examined the contents of the cupboards, which surprised him considerably. Verity had laid in a considerable stock of health foods, which had been somewhat neglected since she left. Resenting anything in the nature of waste, he unearthed her vegetarian cookery book and began concocting tasty little snacks outside regular mealtimes from the contents of the stock cupboard. He even mastered the secret of making omelettes from powdered eggs.

Some weeks, he gave Erika two or three half-days, and enjoyed himself immensely during her absence. Gillian was often out with Harold, too, so he had the place to himself. He was beginning to toy with the idea of inviting two or three of his golf club cronies to a special bachelor dinner which he had cooked entirely himself. Something deep down inside him was for ever urging him to strive for complete independence of all womankind.

He took to darning his socks and sewing on buttons; he had, at least, acquired the knack of this during the First World War, and discovered that it was soon remembered.

On the day Gillian went to see her mother to break the news of his latest activities, Pleydell took the car and drove to St. Albans, where he arranged to join the pottery class at the start of its new term. He had decided against a serious study of water colours for the time being, for that seemed a trifle beyond his present capacity.

While he was in St. Albans he bought a box of mixed dyes, and on his return went straight into the kitchen to experiment with them. Erika was taking a half-day off, so he had the kitchen to himself. When Gillian returned two hours later he was still there, with every bowl and bucket available filled with a startling variety of colours. He displayed a shirt which seemed to her a sickly shade of green.

"What do you think of this?" he inquired.

"Ghastly."

He eyed it thoughtfully. "Of course, it'll look better in a strong light. And it'll dry a shade lighter, of course. It's an experiment really. I mixed the colours myself."

"So I see."

"If it doesn't come out right, I can easily change it to something darker," he assured her.

"Well, I suppose it makes a change from banking," she murmured, taking off her gloves. "I wish the chairman could see you now."

He grinned a trifle ruefully. "Ah well, I'd no idea art and colour and so on could be so fascinating," he said. "I'm starting pottery in a fortnight." He hesitated, then said rather cautiously: "By the way, I had another idea today. I thought it might be fun to grow a beard."

Gillian blinked at him. He didn't even talk like his old self any more, but used a lot of odd phrases he had picked up from Nick.

"Don't you think it might suit me?"

She shook her head. "I think you've left it rather late. Beards should be grown when a man's young." She had read this in a book, but had no idea if it was true.

"What's age got to do with it?" he demanded. "Nick says it would be quite distinguished."

"So it's Nick who's been putting these ideas into your head," she replied, edging into the one vacant corner of the kitchen and sitting down.

"I'm quite capable of thinking for myself," he said a trifle stiffly. "You don't seem to realize that there's been quite a revolution in my life these past few months. Compared with what has already happened to me, growing a beard is simply child's play. In fact, you could almost describe it as the finishing touch. If your mother were here, I'm sure she would be delighted."

"I'm afraid she wouldn't. I've just seen Mother, and she's quite worried about all these recent developments."

"She should have thought of that before she started arranging a divorce. Now we are separated, she surely doesn't expect me to let her rule my life."

He gave one of his bowls a stir with obvious relish.

"Please, Daddy, don't grow it before the wedding," she

begged, with a note of concern. "I'd hate to be given away by the poor man's Augustus John."

He considered this with a thoughtful frown.

"It might look quite distinguished," he insisted, "particularly if I recited a poem specially written in honour of the occasion."

"But you don't write poetry," she pointed out.

"Every civilized man who's been in love has written poetry. You'll find Harold will get round to it," he told her. "I wrote quite a lot about the time I first met your mother. Orthodox stuff, of course . . . full of rhymes."

"How delightfully quaint. All the same, I don't suppose Mother will like the idea of another writer in the family."

He energetically wrung out a shirt he had just dyed an unusual shade of orange. "I'm not in the same family as your mother any more," he reminded her. "That divorce caused me a lot of trouble, and I don't like to think it was completely wasted. In fact, I'm beginning to think it wasn't at all a bad idea. I met that bounder Wilkinson yesterday, and it gave me great satisfaction to point out to him that I'm no longer in the running for super-tax. And I think I'm settling down rather well to this happy-go-lucky sort of existence, considering I was cooped up in an office for a quarter of a century."

"All the same, I'm a little surprised you let Mother talk you into it. You've given up your job and your social position——"

"I've been trying to tell you that this business has had its compensations. And when you get to my age you are prepared to make a lot of sacrifices for peace and quiet."

"But you were a man who was used to responsibility; well known in Firbright; handling thousands of pounds every day——"

"It's nice to be free of that responsibility."

His voice sounded convincing enough, but he couldn't help wishing she would leave the subject, so he started making a great clatter with his bowls.

"I wonder what one does with this dye when it's finished with?" he mused. "I suppose it has to be thrown away."

"Well, it's cheap enough, and you certainly can't leave it all over the kitchen like that. Erika will have a fit when she gets back. Clear it away now, and I'll make some coffee."

"No, no; I'll make it," he insisted, reaching for the coffee-pot.

Gillian wandered into the next room, and two minutes later returned with a note she had found propped on the mantel-piece.

"I'm afraid we've seen the last of Erika," she said.

He looked up inquiringly. "You mean she isn't coming back?"

"That's about it. According to this note, she seems to have eloped with her boy friend, the cinema operator!"

CHAPTER XIV

PLEYDELL IN ARCADIA

DURING the month before the decree nisi was finalized Verity threw herself into her work and contrived to finish her new book, which she called *Desert Symphony*. It had somehow seemed a much greater task now she was doing it for a living; she experienced similar sensations to those of an official whose hitherto voluntary efforts are suddenly rewarded by a handsome salary. Money had an extraordinary knack of taking the flavour out of things and of imbuing one with a deadly sense of obligation.

Time and again she reproved herself for allowing stray thoughts of Pleydell to drift between her and her story; she could not help wondering how he was getting on without Erika to look after the house. Gillian was too engrossed with preparation for her wedding and the life to follow to spend much time at home, and they were struggling along with the help of a Mrs. Packwood, one of the bank's charwomen who came in for two hours in a morning after she had finished cleaning the office.

Mrs. Packwood was all very well in her way, but she needed some direction and supervision, and Verity had long since taken it for granted that such functions were her supreme prerogative, that no one else in the house was even remotely capable of them. She could not bring herself to realize that Gillian was perfectly competent to fulfil that function, and that it would prove an admirable introduction to the domestic routine of married life.

However, the book was presently finished and she took it herself round to the publishers, where she found Paskin, urbane as ever, full of ideas for launching more publicity drives and Press stunts.

"I must have a little peace for a week or two," she stipulated. "I've all sorts of private matters to straighten out, and I don't want reporters and people around me. I think I'm entitled to a little time to myself."

"Of course," he nodded. "We needn't launch any campaign for five or six weeks at the earliest; there'll be a cheaper edition of *The Passionate Mirage* out about that time." He opened his diary and made one or two notes.

She arrived in Firbright one warm afternoon without having warned anyone of her intentions. In all her intercourse with Pleydell she had found the element of surprise invaluable, and that she usually had her way without too much trouble when she presented a *fait accompli*. Both in his banking and private life Pleydell approached every new project with excessive caution, but when one was faced with a bad debt or bankruptcy the only thing was to shrug one's shoulders and make the best of it. Similarly, when something strange came along in the domestic routine, the best course was to arrange to accommodate oneself to it.

All the same, she experienced a slight qualm as she drove through the outskirts of the town. From what Gillian told her, she would have a very different Andrew to deal with; he might react in quite an unexpected manner to this surprise visit.

To her dismay, when she arrived the house was deserted. She blamed herself for not giving notice of her visit. There was nothing to do but wait. She had no key, so she walked round the garden for a while. Obviously, the man who had come to work in it twice a week was still doing so, for it was reasonably well kept. Almost automatically, she stooped and pulled a couple of weeds out of the borders.

The garage was empty; Gillian or her father had obviously taken the car. Verity walked round to the front of the house again, climbed back into her car and thought for a moment. Should she sit and read the book of Whitman's poems she always kept in the car for such occasions? She opened the book and turned the pages, then closed it again. Somehow, she wasn't in the mood for Whitman.

She pressed the starter and drove back to the town. It was nearly four o'clock and she made for the Blue Pantry, a café she had visited from time to time for some years. It was mid-week and rather quiet, so she saw no one she knew when she entered. A waitress in a smart blue cap and apron came up and took her order. The girl was a stranger to her; she wondered why even the best restaurants rarely kept their waitresses for more than a few months nowadays.

Verity would have liked to have seen someone she knew; she felt almost like a stranger visiting the town for the first time. So much had happened since she was last there; she had herself changed so appreciably that it was a little surprising to find the tempo of life in Firbright apparently much the same.

If anything, the place seemed rather smaller and the people more noticeably provincial, but she realized that this was because she was seeing them from a new angle. She wondered vaguely if she could ever settle down again in the place for any length of time; in any case, her old enthusiasm for playing her part in its social life seemed to have evaporated. She realized that in the eyes of the people who counted her divorce would negative all her success in any other sphere so far as social eligibility was concerned. She had been written off as one of those bohemian artistic types, to be regarded with open suspicion.

In her day Verity had overcome a considerable amount of indifference and opposition, but now she suddenly felt lonely. She began to realize that a good, solid husband with a position in the life of the community is an indispensable background to a woman who wishes to assert herself in the social activities of a small country town.

Feeling more than a trifle sorry for herself, she gazed gloomily out of the window at the narrow High Street, which was losing much of its character as the chain stores slowly suppl nted the old family shops, replacing the solid Victorian and Edwardian frontages with chromium-plated monstrosities that never failed to attract the crowds. There were two new ones since she had last been there, and they seemed even more repellent than their predecessors. The entire country was slowly becoming Americanized in the worst possible taste, she told herself.

She found some slight consolation in the fact that the Blue Pantry's well-known China tea had lost none of its fragrance, and was just pouring a second cup when she heard a startled exclamation just behind her. She had obviously been recognized by a man who was climbing the stairs with a young lady. She swung round in her chair and saw that it was Pleydell.

He looked ill at ease, but it was too late to turn back now, and he came to the top of the stairs, near Verity's table. Just one step behind him was a young woman whose black, close-fitting hat, smothered with pink flowers of no recognizable origin, made Verity recoil at once.

From the first few seconds when her searching glance swept the newcomer from top to toe, Verity took a dislike to her, but tried to postpone her judgement, telling herself that the fact that the girl was obviously at least fifteen years younger than her had possibly upset her assessment. She summoned all her self-control and switched on her most charming manner.

"Why, Andrew, how lucky!" she exclaimed, and managed to sound as if she meant it. "I've come down specially to see you, and I thought perhaps you were away."

Pleydell cleared his throat nervously and said, "Er—may I introduce Miss Digby-Leach—my wife——"

"But you're not married any more, darling," simpered his companion, in accents of mingled honey and venom.

Pleydell looked cautiously round the café to see whether anyone had heard her, but there were only two old ladies in a distant corner, who were apparently immersed in their own conversation.

"You must forgive my ex-husband, Miss Digby-Leach," said Verity smoothly. "We were married a very long time you know. Do come and sit down." She pulled out two chairs at her table, and all the time her brain was working furiously to think where she had seen this woman before. She had been meeting far too many people lately, she told herself, and her brain no longer retained its old facility for associating names and faces.

Then quite suddenly she did remember. The last time she had seen those piquant features was when they stared up at her amidst a pile of papers and documents relating to her divorce. For once in a way, Verity found herself completely at a loss for a remark to fit the situation.

CHAPTER XV

RETURN OF THE CUCKOO

IT WAS not exactly a cosy tea such as we associate with English traditions. Verity presently recovered sufficiently to keep up a pleasant flow of conversation about her own activities, but she was seething inwardly that Gillian had never telephoned her concerning this startling development.

In actual fact, Gillian was hardly to blame, for she had telephoned twice when Verity was out, and it was not always easy to find a suitable opportunity, with Iris flitting through the house, and appearing unexpectedly to overhear private conversations. Although she had only been there two days, she seemed to have developed an uncanny flair for drifting casually into a room when anything was afoot which was none of her business.

Iris had arrived when Pleydell was in the kitchen preparing lunch. Gillian was out shopping in Firbright, and he was expecting her back at any moment, so that when the front-doorbell rang he thought she had forgotten her key, and went to the door without bothering to remove the apron he was wearing.

For a moment he had not recognized the expensively dressed young woman who was just turning to pay the taxi driver. As the vehicle drove off she suddenly faced him.

"Hallo, darling," she smiled. "Remember me?"

"Iris!" he exclaimed in a half-whisper, fumbling with the tapes of his apron. "What brings you here?"

"Aren't you going to ask me in?"

"Yes, of course."

He led the way into the lounge. By this time he had disengaged himself from the apron, which he flung under a cushion. She settled herself comfortably on the settee, contriving to display a length of shapely leg in the process.

"You don't seem very pleased to see little Iris," she pouted.

"I'm sorry . . . it's such a surprise," he stammered. "I had no idea you were coming. How did you find the address?"

"The solicitors gave it to me; that is, I happened to see it on one of the documents in the case, and I made a note of it at the time. I had a feeling it might come in useful one day."

"I can't think why you should want to see me again," he said somewhat lamely.

"Didn't I tell you at the time you were one of the nicest men I've met. I thought I made that quite clear."

"Yes, you did say something of the sort, but——" He broke off and demanded abruptly, "The solicitors paid you the money, didn't they?"

She nodded. "They always pay up. But since that day I met you I've lost all heart for my work."

"I'm sorry," he said, very much at a loss.

"I just couldn't face it."

She sat there, gripping her handbag, and looking as dejectedly tense as the deserted heroine in a French film. "The way they try to impose on a girl's good nature—it's horrible. . . ." She was talking half to herself, and Pleydell was still completely puzzled. He wished Gillian would come to relieve the tension. " . . . A fortnight ago, I went to Brighton with a stockbroker named—well, never mind his name. He's been divorced twice already, and from what I saw of him he ought to be in a home of some sort. I made him keep his distance for the best of two hours, though it was a hell of a struggle. Then I suddenly got fed up with the whole thing, smacked his face hard and walked straight out. My hand still tingles when I think about it. Anyhow, I daren't go to any of my regular places for another job."

There was a tiny catch in her voice and she wiped away a suspicion of a tear very carefully from the corner of her right eye, neatly avoiding the mascara-ed lashes. "Not that I have any desire to go back. I'd sooner starve," she informed him, defiantly tossing her well-groomed head. Then her voice adopted a new pleading note. "The trouble is I am practically starving," she said pathetically.

Pleydell moved to the door, looking very concerned. "You must stay to lunch; it won't be more than ten minutes," he promised. "I'm glad you reminded me." He already imagined he could smell the potatoes burning.

She followed him into the kitchen and perched on the table, admiring his cooking. "Fancy you having to do all this, you poor thing," she murmured. "You need a housekeeper, you know."

"I rather enjoy it," he was starting to protest, but she waved him aside, insisting that good men were scarce and deserved to be well looked after. He was still no wiser as to the purpose of her visit.

"Shan't be long," he said in what he imagined was a cheerful voice, as he rigorously stirred the gravy and quickly inspected the tart in the oven. "If you're absolutely ravenous, there's some cheese and biscuits in the——"

"I didn't mean I was starved in that way," she interrupted as wistfully as ever.

"Then I don't quite follow what——"

"I meant starved for affection."

"Oh," said Pleydell, again at a loss. He wished she wasn't quite so predatory in her tactics, though he supposed it was understandable in a girl who had been so much on her own, and dependent so completely upon men for her living.

"I'm hard-up, too," she went on. "It isn't easy to get work in my line, unless people know you."

"Couldn't you go back to shorthand-typing?" he suggested mildly.

She shuddered. "That wouldn't keep me in clothes. Besides," she pouted, "I've lost the knack of it now."

Pleydell dexterously tipped out the potatoes into a dish, then turned his attention to the gravy, which he presently decanted into a sauce-boat. "You'll feel better when you've had a good lunch," he consoled her, still more than a little uncertain as to why she should have decided to visit him.

"I'm so sick of London," she murmured, making no attempt to help him with the lunch. "It's nothing but people and traffic and noise. I long to get away from it."

He was about to make some formal reply when the telephone rang. It was Gillian, who told him she would be lunching with Harold, unless he wanted her specially at home. For a moment his brain worked desperately, and he toyed with the idea of begging her to come back as quickly as possible. Then he realized that it wouldn't be any too easy to explain the situation, and it was more than likely Iris could hear every

I

word he said, as he had omitted to close the door after him. He consoled himself that after a heart-to-heart talk over lunch, he would probably be able to drive her back to the station, and Gillian need never know anything about her visit.

All through lunch Iris flattered him as relentlessly as heavy artillery attacks an objective with a preliminary barrage. The flattery was interspersed with woeful tales of how a girl must struggle for existence, of her unending search for the man who really understood. . . .

Pleydell never recalled inviting her to stay for a few days, but by the end of lunch she somehow seemed to be taking it for granted. He found himself conducting her over the house, and she promptly went into such ecstasies over his bedroom that he felt bound to offer it to her. Five minutes later he was a little surprised to hear her telephoning the railway station to arrange for her luggage to be delivered. So she had intended to stay all the time!

He grew more and more perturbed. What was the woman proposing to do? He was more than a little afraid of Iris, because he did not remotely understand her. She represented an unknown quantity. Verity's actions had never been exactly predictable, but over a long period of years he had at least come to recognize a certain pattern in them, and had developed a defence mechanism that was capable of responding to most *contretemps*.

In vain he had tried to put out mild hints that Iris would find Firbright too quiet and provincial, his own company dull and the country very much overrated. She took them all in her stride, insisting that she was really a country girl, and had always remained so at heart. Crossing her shapely nylon-clad legs, she leaned back on the settee and dilated on her quest for a really decent man she could trust as she had found she could trust him. . . . She had had enough of exciting men to last her a lifetime. She had never before met one who was really depend-able. . . . He had no idea how wonderful it was; like coming into harbour after a storm at sea.

Iris seemed prepared to enlarge upon the idea until further notice. "I imagined your home would be exactly like this," she informed him, languidly flicking the ash from her cigarette. She half-closed the mascara-laden lashes and wistfully added, "It's just like a dream come true."

Though he had handled many types of feminine clients in his time, Pleydell was completely at a loss. But he had a shrewd idea that even if he were downright rude to Iris, she would pretend to misunderstand or not to hear him at all. She was the sort who can find offence in the most harmless pleasantry if they were to mount their high horse; yet are able to ignore the most pointed remark that verges upon an insult when they are equally determined to remain on good terms.

Iris had plainly decided to plant herself upon his hospitality and nothing was going to deter her from that purpose. At the same time, she seemed to have convinced herself that she was doing him a favour by coming to keep him company in his hour of need, when wife and family had deserted him. She insisted they would be as happy as two birds in a nest. In the face of her enthusiasm, Pleydell made a feeble attempt to look grateful that would never have deceived an independent observer for a moment.

Presently a taxi arrived with Iris's luggage: three large suitcases and a hat-box. As they were carrying them upstairs, Gillian came in. Pleydell hastily introduced Iris as his solicitor's secretary, who was 'down here for a day or two about the divorce'.

"There's nothing gone wrong, has there?" inquired Gillian anxiously.

"No, no . . . it's just a question of signing papers and so on," her father hastily assured her.

Gillian eyed the cases thoughtfully, obviously speculating upon the necessity for so much luggage on a short business trip. For that matter, why any luggage at all? Surely the business could be settled in an hour or so . . . and would a secretary be qualified to discuss it? She looked at Iris again. Hardly the secretary type, she decided.

"I'm giving Miss Digby-Leach my room," her father was saying. "I'll move into the top room. Could you help me make up the bed?"

Gillian went in search of sheets and blankets, her brain buzzing with this latest development. It was so unlike her father. Surely it couldn't be that he had been associating with this woman for some time, and they were simply waiting for the divorce to be finalized. The visitor seemed to be chattering away in animated fashion to Pleydell in the bedroom; they might have known each other for ages.

When they all returned to the lounge, Gillian imagined once or twice that she intercepted distress signals from her father. And he certainly did not appear to relish being left alone with his guest. Nor would he leave Gillian with Iris for a moment, though she made one or two moves to get him out of the way.

Iris seemed content to follow him around like a devoted lapdog. She went with him into the kitchen to prepare tea, though Gillian volunteered to do it, and remained with him in the lounge afterwards while Gillian washed the dishes. She answered one or two mildly probing questions about her job and her home with complete equanimity, and Gillian grew more and more baffled.

"Where are you going?" Pleydell demanded with patent anxiety, when Gillian came in wearing a summer coat about an hour after tea.

"To the pictures with Harold. I told you I'd be out this evening," she reminded him. "Why don't you come, too?" she added as an afterthought, noting his worried look.

"Oh no," said Iris, "we wouldn't spoil your party."

"All the same, it might be an idea to go out somewhere," said Pleydell with a note of desperation. "We might have dinner at that new roadhouse on the Merrifield by-pass." He thought they would be less likely to be seen three or four miles out of town. Iris fell in with the plan right away, and as soon as Gillian had gone out she went to prepare for the excursion.

Gillian telephoned her mother before she went into the cinema, and also when they came out, but there was no reply. On the way home in Harold's car she confided in him about the events of the afternoon.

"Sounds a bit of a rum go," he decided, frowning thoughtfully. "There's something queer about your old man since the divorce. First, those fads of his; they were harmless enough. But when it comes to young women . . . well, that's a different thing."

There was something so comforting about Harold's view of life, thought Gillian. He had everything divided neatly into sections and labelled. If one told him he was sentenced to die at dawn, he would probably start thinking about insurance. Harold boasted that he liked to keep his feet on the ground.

"Perhaps I ought to come in and see this woman," he said presently, as they turned the last corner.

"Not tonight, darling," Gillian decided quickly. "I'd like to find out a bit more about her first."

"Yes, perhaps that would be best," he replied, having deliberated the matter for a couple of minutes. "I like to know where I stand with people when I'm meeting them."

Gillian kissed him lightly and ran into the front porch, where she fumbled for her latchkey and opened the door, wondering what fresh surprises lay in store for her. But the scene that greeted her gaze appeared entirely uneventful. Pleydell was sitting in his armchair, studying a book on pottery, from which he seemed to have been reading aloud to Iris, who was curled up on the settee lazily smoking. Nevertheless, Gillian could not fail to notice the relieved expression on her father's face as she came into the room.

She managed to get a few words with Pleydell while he was trying to light the kitchen stove the next morning ready for the arrival of the daily woman. He glanced in her direction as she came in, then looked away again rather uncomfortably. Gillian poured herself a cup of tea from the pot he had just made, and went to the point without any further ado.

"I had no idea you were expecting visitors," she began in what she hoped was a casual tone.

"Er—no—it was quite a surprise," he replied, trying to sound equally non-committal.

"She works for the solicitors who handled the divorce?"

He nodded.

"I didn't know you'd been to them before."

"I hadn't. But I've seen them several times during the past year or so. Miss Digby-Leach often dealt with the business. That's how we got to know each other rather well."

Gillian frowned as she stirred her tea. "All the same, it's a little unusual for a solicitor's clerk to arrive on a visit, isn't it?" she suggested.

"She has a few days' leave, and I thought she might like to stay. She's been a bit run down lately," he added lamely.

"Have you any idea how long she's staying?" persisted Gillian.

"Well, no, we haven't exactly discussed it."

Gillian finished her tea and lighted a cigarette, while Pleydell poured a drop of kerosene on the stove and flung a match on it.

"She seems very attractive; hardly the type for a solicitor's office," ventured Gillian presently.

"Girls in London offices are often very smart," he replied, putting on his coat. "Would you like to take her a cup of tea?"

"I'm sure she'd be very disappointed if *you* didn't take it," murmured Gillian, flicking the ash off her cigarette, "and while you're up there, I'll see what's to be done about breakfast."

Pleydell seemed about to make some protest, but she had opened the refrigerator and was already busy.

With a tiny sigh of resignation he poured out the tea and went off upstairs. Outside Iris's door he paused for a moment, then knocked softly.

"Come in, darling," cried a voice that its owner apparently hoped would be audible in every corner of the house.

"Er—I've brought your tea," said Pleydell.

"Well, bring it in, darling. I'm quite respectable."

She was sitting up in bed, wearing the same eau-de-nil négligé she had worn at Redsea Bay. "Remember this?" she asked, pulling it round her shoulders. "I brought it along specially for you."

"Very nice," he muttered, nervously clearing his throat.

"I dare say you got more sleep last night than the other time," she smiled provocatively, as she took the cup and saucer from him. After a couple of sips she set the cup on her bedside table, and stretched luxuriously. "How wonderful to wake up and find oneself in the country!" she enthused. "I've been lying here for ages, listening to the birds."

"If you'll excuse me," he said, "I think I'd better be seeing about breakfast. Mrs. Packwood doesn't get here till nine, and I like to have everything straight for her."

He went downstairs and found that as usual Gillian had boiled the eggs as hard as pebbles, and was now busily engaged in making toast that resembled nothing so much as charcoal. He did not greatly object to hard-boiled eggs, but felt bound to do another one for the guest. After that, he patiently cut more slices of bread for fresh toast.

He hoped Iris would not find the bath water too cold, for the stove had been out for the greater part of the night, and it would take some time to warm. Of course, there was always a chance that she took a cold bath . . . though she hardly looked quite the type.

Iris was wearing a very attractive powder-blue dressing-gown when she came down to breakfast, profusely apologizing for her *déshabillé* when she saw that her host and hostess were fully dressed. But Gillian could not help feeling that she had chosen that attire deliberately; and so it was to prove on subsequent mornings. Iris enjoyed showing herself off in a dressing-gown. She had quite a selection. She tried to make vivacious conversation over breakfast, exclaiming at the glorious morning and how she was looking forward to a real day in the country.

"I warn you we're inclined to be rather dull here since Mother went her ways," said Gillian.

I shall be quite happy to lie in a deck-chair and relax," Iris assured her.

While they were in the middle of breakfast, Mrs. Packwood, the daily woman, arrived and could hardly have appeared more surprised if they had been entertaining Madame Pompadour. Her bulging eyes absorbed Iris's dressing-gown and filmy primrose pyjamas more avidly than anything she saw on the screen at her weekly visits to the Majestic Cinema. While she washed up the breakfast things she gossiped to Gillian, who was cleaning her tennis shoes in a corner by the kitchen stove. They talked in cautious semi-whispers.

"Your dad ain't thinking of gettin' married again already, is he?" demanded Mrs. Packwood, without much beating about the bush.

"Search me," replied Gillian. "Anyhow, I don't think he's known her very long, and in any case she's supposed to be down here on a business visit."

Mrs. Packwood sniffed sceptically, as if to convey that ladies like Iris could be interested in only one sort of business. "Well, I reckon that outfit cost her a tidy penny," she conceded, as if to imply that Iris could not possibly have come by the money honestly. "Still, I reckon your dad can do with somebody to cheer him up a bit. He's been down in the dumps lately. Hardly a word to say for himself."

Lingering over the breakfast table, Iris was doing her utmost to give satisfaction in the rôle of the adoring little woman who listens to her man's verdict on the morning's news, adding comments of approval from time to time. She found that her host was none too eager to discuss the news at all. He had long since become submerged in contempt for the Government, which defied verbal expression, and the only section of the paper that interested him nowadays was the book reviews. Somehow, he didn't feel like discussing books with Iris.

Presently she rose and went off to her room, where she remained for the greater part of the morning, presumably busying herself with her toilet. Gillian went into Firbright to do some shopping, as she would be playing tennis that afternoon. Pleydell moped about, doing one or two little jobs, but he was always on edge, apprehensive that Iris would come down and precipitate some sort of crisis. He couldn't think what exactly, for she had displayed nothing but a very obvious desire to be pleasant and agreeable, but he couldn't help feeling that this was mainly superficial. She was obviously there with some objective in mind, and he hoped it wasn't what he suspected.

To take his mind off her, he went into the kitchen and began to help Mrs. Packwood with the lunch, spending far too much time scraping carrots and peeling potatoes. Even when he had finished that, Iris still had not appeared.

"She'll have to come out of there soon if she wants me to do the room," said Mrs. Packwood in her customary blunt fashion.

"It's all right, Mrs. Packwood," he quickly reassured her. "You can leave the room—I'll do it—or Gillian."

She eyed him suspiciously, but said nothing.

About mid-day, Iris majestically descended the staircase, swinging a large hat, and declared that she could not wait to see the garden, so Pleydell conducted her through the side door and along the gravel path that led past the lawn and into the kitchen garden. As usual, she expressed her delight in everything she saw to the point of positive embarrassment. They settled in a deck-chair until lunch, and the conversation grew rather more desultory, though he still could not contain the feeling that she would make some shattering pronouncement at any second.

Gillian returned in time for lunch and Mrs. Packwood departed. Afterwards, Iris volunteered to help with the domestic chores for the first time, though Gillian suspected that it was because her father had announced his intention of washing the dishes. Iris seemed determined not to be left alone with Gillian just yet awhile anyhow.

In any case, Gillian had to change for tennis, and soon afterwards she went out to get the car. Pleydell felt more desperate than ever; he could not remain alone in the house with Iris throughout the long afternoon. He rushed round to the front to intercept Gillian as she drove round.

"Wait five minutes," he begged, "and we'll come into town with you." Gillian readily agreed.

Back in the house, he was surprised to find that Iris cheerfully acquiesced, and in less than ten minutes Gillian was driving them towards Firbright. Her tennis club was on the opposite side of the town, so she dropped them in the High Street.

On the way into town Pleydell had been unusually silent, wondering what people would say who saw him walking around with Iris. He told himself that for all they knew she might be a relative, or a friend of Gillian. . . . After all, it was a free country, and he had a perfect right to walk around with anyone he chose.

As it happened, Firbright was very quiet, and after Iris had found little to enthuse about in the shops, they decided to walk out to Gillian's tennis club and watch the tournament for an hour. This, of course, would entail meeting people he knew, but as luck would have it Gillian was playing on a distant court, which gave them a good excuse to go and sit over the far side of the enclosure. Iris was bored with the tennis, which she did not understand very well, but it was a pleasant warm afternoon, and there were plenty of frocks for her to admire or criticize. When the pavilion clock struck four Pleydell decided that it would be preferable to stroll back into the town for tea and avoid the crowd in the refreshment bar, so they left Gillian busily engaged in the middle of an apparently unending mixed doubles.

On the way out he had walked past the bank with averted gaze; he had never been inside since the day he left. But on the way back he pointed it out to Iris, and was a little

surprised to find himself discussing it quite casually. Having
received no rebuffs during the afternoon, he was becoming
rather more at ease.

But it was a shock to him to see Verity sitting quietly at
the table near the top of the oak staircase in the Blue Pantry.
She did not seem to have changed in the least, and for a
moment he could hardly believe his eyes. Yet as soon as their
first meeting was over he experienced a definite sense of relief
deep down inside himself. In spite of all her experiences during
the past year, Verity was a comparatively known quantity to
him. It was rather like the family doctor turning up at the end
of a long vigil beside a sick-bed. Here was someone to deal with
the situation; Verity had never been at a loss when it came to
any form of negotiation with her own sex. Even as they talked,
he watched Iris's exuberance fading visibly before her quiet
interrogation.

When Iris rather noticeably went out of her way to inform
Verity that she had spent the night at the house, Verity
showed no sign of disapproval. When Iris showered praise
upon her book, she hardly seemed to hear, though she smiled
pleasantly enough and gravely thanked her. In fact, Pleydell
could never recall having seen Verity so completely master of
a situation. She seemed utterly capable of dealing with any
contingency.

Indeed, Verity gave not the slightest hint of the furnace
that was raging within her. Something—it may have been a
force of habit acquired at cocktail parties, when she had learned
to be pleasant to all comers—compelled her to maintain a
measured conversation, as if she had been taking tea with a
couple of distant acquaintances.

She very quickly arrived at an estimate of Iris, but was
more interested to note any changes in her ex-husband's
appearance or manner during the past few months. He seemed
to be as neatly dressed as ever, though no doubt Iris's presence
had something to do with that. His manner was a trifle
hesitant, but after the first few minutes he was obviously
pleased to see her and patently anxious to be friendly. And
when Iris had vanished into the ladies' cloakroom at the end
of the meal, he leaned over and said quietly, "Verity, you are
coming back with us, aren't you?" There was a look in his
eyes reminiscent of an eager spaniel.

"If you're sure it isn't putting you out at all," she replied
with serious politeness.

He leaned back in his chair and released a deep sigh of
relief. "Thank God for that," he said quietly.

CHAPTER XVI

HOUSE DIVIDED

ON the way home from tennis Gillian stopped at a call-
box to telephone her mother's flat, but again there was no
reply. When she walked into the kitchen and saw Verity and
Pleydell busily preparing dinner, she was so taken aback that
for a moment she could do no more than nod in response to
Verity's greeting. Her mother embraced her much more
warmly than was her custom, and she noticed that her father
looked considerably more relaxed than he had appeared earlier
in the day.

She was relieved to see they were apparently on excellent
terms; that was one crisis temporarily out of the way. At first
she thought Verity's presence had driven Iris away, but she
soon learned that she was up in her room, presumably preparing for a grand entrance just before dinner.

While she paid scrupulous attention to every detail of her
make-up, Iris was turning over the latest developments in her
mind. At first, she wondered if Pleydell had telephoned for
Verity to come down, but she dismissed the idea at once, for
their meeting was so obviously casual. True, Verity had been
on the way, but she did not appear to have apprised anyone
of her intentions.

She wondered vaguely if it had been good policy to leave
Pleydell and Verity alone together. But he had assured her
that night at Redsea Bay that there had been nothing between
them for some time, and surely Verity would have less time
than ever for him nowadays. Yet the fact remained that she
had come down in the midst of her hectic life in Town.
Probably it was some small point in connection with the
divorce, or she may have called to collect some of her personal

things. Though there was really no need for her to stay the night, as she appeared to be doing.

Still, they were bound to get together sooner or later, and Iris preferred to concentrate upon making herself attractive in the time available before dinner. She had a fifteen years' advantage on Verity at least, and from her experience of men she knew that Pleydell was at an age when he would be likely to appreciate it. Not many men around fifty had a glamorous young woman in her middle-twenties flinging herself at their heads. How could any reasonably normal man help but succumb?

She unstoppered a tiny scent bottle labelled 'Belle Amie', moistened the tip of her slim index finger with the contents and dabbed lightly around her neck and ears.

Down in the kitchen, Verity lifted the lid of a casserole and sniffed appreciatively.

"It's been cooking practically all day," her late husband informed her.

"Delicious," she nodded, replacing the lid. "You've learnt something at any rate since we separated."

"Men are better cooks than women when they care to give their mind to it," he maintained. "They study it as an art; not as a matter of necessity."

"They don't have to regard it as a life sentence," she could not help retorting.

He sniffed and said, "The milk's burning," before the argument could develop.

During dinner Iris and Verity eyed each other from opposite sides of the table, and continued to manœuvre for position like two boxers seeking an opening at the start of a first round.

"Isn't it wonderful to be really in love for the very first time?" Iris asked Gillian, as if they were sharing a mutual experience.

Gillian found herself blushing and in her embarrassment began to chatter about her tennis matches of the afternoon. Soon afterwards Iris began to discuss a current newspaper scandal.

"I can't think why people are so shocked because a middle-aged man turns to a girl fifteen or twenty years younger than himself," she announced. "It's perfectly natural that he should want to renew his youth; most men are boys at heart, don't you think?"

She looked pointedly at Pleydell, who turned his attention assiduously to his figs and custard, and refused to meet her gaze.

"I always thought youth called to youth," suggested Verity indifferently.

"Ah, now you're speaking as a novelist, aren't you? Of course, the public likes to read about that sort of thing in books, but in real life it's so different, don't you think?"

"Old men are always making fools of themselves . . . in and out of books," replied Verity somewhat cryptically.

"By the way," put in Pleydell hastily, "I forgot to ask you how your new novel is getting on."

"I finished it two days ago."

"Do tell us all about it," begged Iris, scenting further openings for pointed references to big romance.

"Oh, it's just another tale of the desert," replied Verity somewhat wearily. "No relation to real life, but what the public likes to read . . , I hope."

"But you get your characters from life, don't you?" persisted Iris. "I've seen pictures of you in the papers with such a handsome sheik. Do tell us all about him."

"That was just a publicity stunt. I hardly know him at all."

Iris could not conceal her disappointment, though she was obviously sceptical. Scenting danger, Pleydell changed the conversation once again.

"I saw Wilkinson last week," he told Verity.

"The income tax inspector?"

"Yes, it gave me great pleasure to remind him that we wouldn't be liable for super-tax now. At least, I won't."

"I hope you made it all quite clear to him," said Verity. "He knew about our divorce?"

"Oh yes; he saw it in the local paper, and seemed to have enjoyed it."

"He would. He's the sniggering type."

"I knew quite a nice income tax man once," offered Iris, anxious to remain in the conversation. "We—er—met in a hotel at Brighton."

"Did he explain all about excess rents and unearned income?" inquired Verity somewhat acidly.

"No, he told me all about himself. His marriage had been a mistake, and he was very anxious to get back to his mother. That man simply worshipped his mother."

"How very unfortunate for you!" Verity could not help remarking.

Gillian quickly interposed, "You won't have to pay super-tax, will you, Mother?"

"I don't think so. I've been to a good accountant, who tells me I get all sorts of allowances. I can even put down the cost of a trip to Egypt to get information for my books."

"But you haven't been to Egypt."

"That's what I told him, but he said how is the Inland Revenue Department to know that. They're much too busy checking on black marketeers to bother to trace my movements."

"I dare say that's true enough," nodded her husband.

"How nice to have to worry about super-tax," sighed Iris enviously. "I'm afraid I'll never get that near the top income level."

"All the same, I hope you didn't taunt Wilkinson too much," said Verity to Pleydell. "I never liked the look of the man, and I'm sure he could be very nasty."

"Well, you won't come under this area for income tax any more, will you?" asked Iris.

"But of course," replied Verity sweetly. "I shall probably be staying here for some time."

Iris looked round the little group with an air of complete bewilderment. For a moment, Verity almost felt sorry for her.

"You mean you are both going on living here . . . together?" she stammered, her mascara-ed lashes working overtime.

"Why not?" said Verity.

"But . . . I don't understand. . . ."

"It's quite simple," explained Verity. "We got our divorce for purely financial reasons, and now it's absolute we find it convenient to continue to share the same house. We're used to each other's ways, we like this house, and we know the district. And I shall be able to see that Gillian is married in style."

Iris swung round on Pleydell. "Is this true?" she demanded.

"That's what we arranged," he told her.

Iris frowned. "It doesn't make sense to me," she declared. "Why get divorced and then go on living together?"

"We're not living together—at least, not what you mean. . . ."

"You mean not sleeping together?" queried Iris bluntly.

"I don't see that our private affairs concern you," replied Verity with a shrug.

"Oh, but they do," insisted Iris, all restraint flung to the winds. "You seem to forget I was co-respondent in your divorce case. I spent a night with your husband."

There was a tiny exclamation from Gillian. So that's who Iris is, she thought. Why hadn't her father told her so last night? Why hadn't Iris? What *was* going on? Surely her father wasn't really attracted by Iris.

"I don't see that there's any need to go into that," Verity was saying.

Iris turned to Pleydell. "Is that what you think?" she demanded.

"Well, it's all rather complicated," he began to hedge.

"You haven't forgotten that night, have you?" interrupted Iris. "That wonderful night at Redsea Bay."

"I'll never forget that night," declared Pleydell piously, though Verity detected a certain ambiguity in his tone.

This was the first time since they met at tea that Iris had lost her cooing complacency. Verity watched her closely. Surely she wasn't really in love with Andrew? The whole idea was quite ridiculous. But if she were not attracted to him, then why had she come all this way as soon as the divorce was made absolute? If it was just a straightforward case of gold-digging, then it was obviously her duty to see that Pleydell was not exploited.

She turned to Iris once more. "I'm sorry if you're disappointed, Miss Digby-Leach. You see how things are between Andrew and myself. This is exactly how we planned everything; I should have thought he would have explained that. Now, if you feel you'd sooner go back in the morning and cut short your visit, there's a good train at ten-eight."

Pleydell went quietly over to the sideboard and poured himself another glass of sherry. Iris looked across at him.

"Do you want me to go?" she asked.

He took a sip at the sherry. He didn't really mind how long

Iris stayed so long as Verity was here. Maybe they would cancel each other's shortcomings, which would be most agreeable. And they would certainly chaperone each other in the event of any scandal. The more he considered the idea, the more intriguing it sounded. It looked as if life were going to be considerably more interesting from now on.

As he sipped his sherry he tried to estimate how the arrangement would work out. Of course, there was no telling what situations would arise, but he had a feeling that Iris would be a buffer against any awkwardness from Verity, who, in her turn, was fully capable of negativing any of Iris's tendencies towards rather sickly sentimentalizing. Putting it crudely, they might batter themselves against each other, leaving him in comparative peace.

Never before had Verity even suspected that he might be attractive to another woman, and if Iris could arouse a few doubts in her mind on this score, then Verity might well prove more reasonable in the future. She had had things too much her own way in the past; he could see that now. She had taken far too much for granted, assuming her right to a circle of artistic men friends, while he was supposed to be completely satisfied with his business acquaintances.

As for Iris, she was obviously on very strange territory, and did not know what to make of Verity at all. One aspect shocked her, for she had been inclined to assume that Verity was just another middle-class wife, who had dominated her husband to the point of distraction. Verity's unorthodox proposal about their living together after the divorce had plainly startled Iris, and completely changed the picture for her. She was now feeling her way very cautiously.

He drained his glass and set it down carefully.

"Do you want me to go?" Iris asked him again.

He shook his head slowly. "If you like it here, then stay by all means," he said.

It was Verity's turn to appear taken aback. "Andrew! You're not inviting her to stay indefinitely?"

"There's plenty of room," he murmured. "I have a feeling that you two might be rather good for each other.

CHAPTER XVII

HERE COMES THE BRIDE

FOR some days there was a strained atmosphere of veiled hostility, with Verity and Iris remaining scrupulously polite to each other, and as considerate to Pleydell as a Mormon's two favourite wives vying for his favours. He appeared to revel in this new situation; he was in the lucky position of a nation that controls the balance of power. However, Gillian could see that her mother was feeling the strain more than Iris, who was leading a comparatively sheltered existence for the first time in years, and rather enjoying this novel experience. She felt no great responsibility, and her only real concern was not to antagonize Pleydell. This was not unduly difficult, for he was in quite a mellow mood since the arrival of Verity.

At first it seemed doubtful how Iris would fit into the Pleydell household, but she somehow contrived it without any great fuss. She went out of her way to be friendly towards Gillian, who was nearest her own age, and who could often spare the time for a shopping expedition into Firbright or even into London, for she was somewhat laboriously getting together her bottom drawer in readiness for the approaching wedding. Iris had an extensive knowledge of the London dress shops which offered the best value in various lines of clothing, and she was quite ready to share her information.

Iris had a pleasing line of small-talk with her own sex, and Gillian soon became reconciled to the visitor's 'past', which in course of conversation seemed to take on a much more roseate hue than when considered in terms of the police court or solicitors' office. Indeed, before long, Gillian often found herself envying Iris her varied experiences and wide knowledge of the human male. Iris's world revolved around men, and she magnified their importance so persistently that there were times when Gillian felt vaguely alarmed about her own impending alliance with one of them.

Once or twice Pleydell and Iris accompanied Gillian and Harold to the cinema or out to a meal at a restaurant. Verity was busy with a series of articles for a woman's paper which

K

involved some research and occupied much of her time, so she was not often free to make such expeditions. Nevertheless, she watched the others depart with a certain feeling of envy. Pleydell seemed nearly twenty years younger just lately, and Verity felt rather out of things.

She was more than a little perturbed about Pleydell's apparent rejuvenation; to her there was something unnatural in the change. He said the most unexpected things at times, particularly when Iris was present, and on some occasions he seemed to lack his former dependability and solid sense of reason. She could not endure his flippancies, which reminded her of an elephant's painful attempts at a polka. There were times when she thought there might be something wrong with his glands, and once or twice she was on the verge of suggesting he should visit a specialist.

But Verity no longer spoke her thoughts without consideration to Pleydell. There was always a certain restraint in her conversation with him nowadays. Sometimes she caught herself making a conscious effort to be pleasant towards him; an effort such as she had never made since the days before their marriage. It was not surprising that Pleydell suddenly found life more agreeable than he had known it for years. Such a transformation was calculated to renew any man's youth.

He had a feeling that this golden interim could not possibly endure, but he had cultivated a new outlook which was based upon a 'sufficient unto the day' philosophy, and which seemed to fit his present condition admirably. Looking back upon his banking career, he discovered that he had wasted a lot of time preparing for the worst contingencies, which very rarely happened.

Iris had been at the house just over a fortnight when Gillian returned from meeting Harold one evening with her eyes alight and her cheeks flushed. "Harold thinks he can get a house," she informed the family circle. Verity was sitting on the settee drinking Ovaltine, while Iris and Pleydell had a tea-tray between them in their armchairs.

"Really?" said Verity, glad of a little excitement to relieve what had been rather a boring evening for her. "Whereabouts is the house?"

"In Chestnut Drive. There's some people going abroad;

they asked his firm to sell it for them, and they'll be satisfied if they get £2,500."

"They must be fools," declared Pleydell, who knew the district. "Those houses are worth at least £3,000 nowadays. Probably fetch more at an auction."

Iris looked at him admiringly. "I wish I could talk about property and money right off, just like that," she murmured.

"The point is," continued Gillian hurriedly, "that if Harold can raise the money tomorrow, he'll close the deal, and he thinks we ought to get married right away and move in."

"What's the hurry?" asked Verity.

"Well, the people go abroad next week, and the house will be standing empty.

"Here, steady on," protested Pleydell. "You can't rush off and get married in five minutes."

"Harold suggested a month," said Gillian.

"That doesn't give us much time," mused Verity. "There'll be lots to do."

"I've got quite a few things——"

"And I'll help you," interrupted Iris excitedly. "I'm quite good at altering dresses and running up things. . . . It'll be fun!"

"But I wanted you to get married from the flat in Chelsea," said Verity, "and we can't possibly arrange it all in that time. You'd have to live there for a month to start with. . . ."

"Harold says he'd much sooner get married here. He doesn't seem to fancy a grand London wedding, and you know his people are very friendly with Canon Fosdick. He wants him to marry us."

Pleydell poured himself another cup of tea. "No reason why you shouldn't be married from here that I can see," he murmured. "You can invite your London friends down here, Verity, if you want to. We can hold the reception at the White Hart, or perhaps the Feathers, if they're the sort who'd prefer an old-world place."

"It would have been such a pretty wedding in the Chelsea parish church," said Verity wistfully.

"But it will be a lovely wedding here, darling," argued Iris, who somehow felt more sure of an invitation if it were held in Firbright. "The old church here is beautiful, with all that ivy on the tower. And it's only right she should be married where she has lived all her life. Besides, how would she be able to get the house ready if she were living in Town?"

In face of Iris's arguments and Gillian's persuasion, Verity eventually gave way, though she managed to convey the impression that she was making a tremendous sacrifice, as indeed she felt she was, for she had always had the idea of a fashionable wedding at the back of her mind, and of course it would not be the slightest use inviting the guests to Firbright who would have attended in Chelsea. One or two rather more personal friends, perhaps. . . .

"Isn't it exciting!" enthused Iris. "I haven't been to a really nice wedding for ages."

"A month's no time at all," said Verity. "We'll be rushed off our feet."

"We'll get through somehow," Pleydell assured her. "Iris will help. And if the house isn't quite ready, we can always put them up here for a few days. Then there'll be the extra fortnight during the honeymoon to get the place straight. I've got plenty of time on my hands, and I dare say I'll be able to get through quite a lot of work of one sort and another. There's three of us here, and Harold's family; we've only to pull together."

"You know nothing of the amount of work a big wedding involves," Verity told him.

"Then let's have a small wedding."

"We are not having a hole-and-corner affair," declared Verity firmly. "I shall pay for it myself, and I don't care if it costs five hundred pounds."

"Neither of us is exactly popular in the town at the moment," he ventured. "Don't you think people will talk if there's a lot of fuss and display?"

"Let them talk," said Verity defiantly. "If you're afraid of local gossip, then let's have the wedding in London."

"No, no," he replied hastily. "She's our only child, and I agree that we ought to do the thing in style."

"Of course you must," approved Iris. "It's more likely to impress the local people than turn them against you. I've always found that if other folks think you're on top of the world, then they're on your side."

At last Gillian managed to get in a word. "I don't really mind what sort of wedding it is, or where it takes place," she said. "But there's no need to rush into making plans until Harold has settled about the house. I just thought I'd warn you in good time, but there is a chance the whole thing may fall through."

"There's no harm in making plans," said her father. "You'll be getting married sometime, I suppose, so at least we'll have them in reserve."

"Yes, it's fun to make plans," agreed Iris adoringly.

"Talking of plans," said Verity, opening her handbag and taking out a letter, "I heard from Erika this morning. She wants to come back here."

"But what about that man she ran away with? Won't he marry her?" asked Pleydell.

"It seems there's a little trouble with the law."

"You mean he is married already?" put in Iris, with her rapid comprehension of such *contretemps*.

"That's it, I'm afraid. What's more, he appears to have decided that he prefers his wife."

"Poor Erika!" murmured Gillian. "She seems to have a fatal attraction for married men."

"All the same," said Pleydell, "it's a bit of a nerve, asking you to have her back, after she sloped off like that."

"Foreigners look at these things differently," Verity told him. "All the same, if we're going to have a wedding on our hands, we should find Erika very useful in more ways than one."

"It seems to me she's more than capable of running away with the bridegroom," said Pleydell.

"You needn't worry about that," said Gillian confidently. "The only real problem is where she will sleep."

"You can move out of her room and share with me," decided Verity. "Then that's settled. I'll write and tell her she can come back."

Harold telephoned the next morning to say that he had paid a deposit on the house, and had no difficulty in securing a loan from a building society with which his firm had done business for some years. So the preparations for the wedding began in real earnest.

Verity had to admit that Iris was not boasting of her skill with the needle. She cheerfully tackled a dozen assorted jobs in the course of a day, and could always be relied upon to match colours and materials. She was much more up to date than either Verity or Gillian so far as the latest fashions were concerned, and she invariably came up with a suggestion to solve most of their problems. In fact, Verity and Iris forgot most of their animosity towards each other in their battle against time, for the banns were to be read the following Sunday, and after that they would have just under a month.

Pleydell spent the better part of an afternoon composing a discreetly worded announcement for the local paper and two of the leading Conservative dailies.

He found that the approaching wedding provided a very plausible reason for Verity's presence in the house, when he had to explain to friends that his ex-wife was staying with him. He let them conclude, usually without explanation on his part, that Verity was back home to prepare for her daughter's wedding. If he had to further account for the fact that she was staying on after the wedding, he would deal with that contingency when it arose.

The day after the announcement of the wedding had been published Erika returned, as full of self-assurance as ever ("One would think she'd been paying a visit to a maiden aunt," said Verity), and flung herself cheerfully into the wedding preparations. She seemed almost indifferent about her young man's unfaithfulness; indeed she apparently took it for granted.

"They always go back to their wives," she told Gillian. "I have found that out before. But this time I did not know about the wife until after we had been living together in Salisbury for over a week. So the first time we quarrelled I left him, before I got too fond of him. For two months I was a waitress in a café, but I got tired of old men stroking my knees, so I write and ask your mother if I could come back."

"And what about your—er—friend?" asked Gillian. "Is he back in Firbright?"

Erika shook her head. "I do not know." She had obviously written him off.

"Do you know if his wife has taken him back?"

Erika shrugged. "The wives always take them back. That is what wives are for."

"Thanks for the warning," said Gillian drily.

"But your husband will be different," put in Erika hastily.

"How do you know that?"

"I have seen him looking at you. He will never run after other women." She finished the last piece of silver she had been polishing. "I am so glad your mother had me back," she smiled, replacing the silverware in its case. "It is such fun to live in a house where there will be a wedding. Everything is quite different—there is excitement, gaiety, romance. . . ."

"I'm afraid there's a lot of hard work as well."

Erika laughed. "Birthdays, weddings, funerals—they all mean hard work; especially for the women. But it is work that must be done, and it has its—what do you call it—compensations?"

"I suppose so," nodded Gillian, who was secretly amazed that Erika contrived to remain so cheerful in the midst of all her ups and downs. "All the same, I feel practically worn out already, and there's over a fortnight to go before the wedding yet, with heaps to be done."

There had already been several impromptu family conferences on the question of invitations. They were anxious that no one should be left out, and in addition to their relatives, who were comparatively few and distant, they each had a wide circle of acquaintances, particularly Verity, who wrote down forty-seven names straight off, almost without stopping to think. The first rough list comprised one hundred and twenty-eight names, and it became obvious that the catering facilities at the hotel were going to be taxed to capacity.

From time to time there were fitful arguments, chiefly because Verity wanted to invite casual acquaintances whom she thought might be useful to her, or because Pleydell insisted upon asking a former client whom she considered a profound bore. When the number of potential guests had passed the hundred mark, Harold came in one evening with a list of forty more, his own family's relatives and friends.

"But the Feathers say they can't manage more than a hundred. What are we to do?" asked Gillian.

"Don't worry. Lots of them won't turn up; they'll be too mean to buy a present," Harold informed her. "I'm talking about my lot now—I don't know about yours."

"We'll take a chance," said Verity. "I've thought of three more today. . . . I made a note . . ." And she began looking through the papers in her writing-desk.

A familiar bulky packet caught her eye and she thrust it resolutely into a drawer. But she knew she would have to deal with it soon. It had arrived the previous day, and contained the first batch of proofs of the new novel, with an urgent request for their return as soon as she had corrected them. Luckily, she had finished her series of articles, but the proofs would keep her busy for some time, just when she wanted to devote all her energies to the wedding.

However, she had managed to organize it with her customary efficiency. Pleydell was looking after the catering and other arrangements at the Feathers; Gillian was sending out the invitations; Iris was supervising the dresses, running errands and doing innumerable jobs that seemed to be for ever arising. Although Verity had assigned herself no active tasks, she was continually interrupted at her writing by one of the others who wanted her opinion or advice on the various minor crises which seem to accompany every large wedding so inevitably.

Someone's hand had to be at the controls. Pleydell occasionally needed driving into some activity or other which he was inclined to let slide; Gillian had a knack of vanishing for hours at a time to the new house, just when her presence was required at home, and leaving no hint of her whereabouts; while Iris's taste in dress, though in many ways artistic, was inclined to be a trifle too dashing for Firbright, and needed a certain toning down, if bride and bridesmaids were not to be rendered highly selfconscious.

A week later the presents began to arrive by every post, thus posing yet another problem. They had to be opened, listed, then stored away safely until they could be displayed in the reception room at the Feathers. Some days salad bowls, flower vases and fish-knives seemed to be showering down from heaven as profusely as the manna descended upon the children of Israel. It would take Gillian, aided spasmodically by Pleydell and Iris, the better part of the morning to deal with the influx.

"This is getting like the Christmas rush at the Post Office," he said one morning, as he sorted over the heap that had just arrived, and examined one or two of the labels.

"Wedding presents don't seem to change very much over the years," he mused. "One or two more electric toastmakers, perhaps, instead of toast-racks; an electric percolator in place of the old-fashioned spirit lamp . . . not much imagination."

"I think it's lovely to have so many friends," sighed Iris enviously, as she carefully untied one of the parcels, "and I'm sure it's going to be a perfectly gorgeous wedding."

As the day approached, however, Gillian felt more and more like an actress who is facing the biggest rôle of her career, none too sure of her part, and begins to entertain some doubts as to whether her leading man has been miscast. During the day she was too busy to brood upon the problem, but when excitement kept her awake her doubts grew to enormous proportions.

Yet every day made the event a degree more inevitable. The theatre was engaged, the company contracted, the dresses nearly complete, the properties ready, the house sold out, the stage staff drilled and awaiting their cue and the critics sitting back expectantly.

The curtain must rise to schedule after the overture; the audience must be given some sort of performance; furore or flop; curtain-calls or cat-calls; adulation or recriminations— the show must go on, as inexorably as a mammoth Drury Lane musical.

CHAPTER XVIII

UNEXPECTED GUEST

AT nine-thirty on her wedding morning Gillian was balancing precariously on two legs of a straight-backed chair as she telephoned Pamela Runnels, her chief bridesmaid. A gleam of watery sunlight illuminated the confusion of the breakfast table, which Erika had not yet cleared.

Gillian was still in her dressing-gown, her hair was untidy and face quite devoid of make-up. She had telephoned Pam about some minor hitch in the delivery of the bridesmaids' bouquets, but continued to gossip in a brittle tone which betrayed her excitement, pushing back her unruly hair from time to time with her expensively manicured right hand.

"Four electric toasters," she was informing her bridesmaid, who was inquiring about the presents. "They're all on display at the Feathers; it looks rather like a trades exhibition. I told Harold we're going to eat an awful lot of toast after we're married."

There was a high-pitched giggle from the other end, and Miss Runnels inquired how Harold was standing the strain.

"Oh, he's all right," replied Gillian, as if Harold's was the merest walking-on part in the proceedings. "He's full of clumsy innuendoes about first nights and things. I think he's a bit scared really."

"Aren't you?" came the unmistakable query from Miss Runnels.

"I might have been if I hadn't had a heart-to-heart talk with Iris. She relieved my mind about lots of things. You know she isn't such a bad sort. I was a bit scared that she would get her claws into Daddy, but he doesn't seem to fall for her."

There was a gurgle from the other end of the line.

"Oh no; it isn't that," said Gillian. "She's got all a woman needs in that line. It's just that Daddy has never quite fallen out of love with Verity. And the more she provokes him, the better he seems to like it. I've never known such a glutton for punishment." She tilted forward on her chair, recovered and said: "This is a dreadful conversation for a wedding morning. Darling, I must fly. I haven't done a thing to my face yet, and my hair looks like one of those horrible low comedy wigs. Don't be late at the church, or I'll never speak to you again."

She replaced the receiver and turned to see her mother had just come into the room, dressed ready to go out.

"Good heavens, Gillian, you aren't half ready," Verity said when she caught sight of her.

"There's over two hours yet. Heaps of time."

She looked at her mother dubiously for a moment, then asked, "Is everything all right?"

"I've attended to everything," Verity assured her.

"I just had a peculiar sort of feeling that something might go wrong."

"What should go wrong?"

"I don't know. Things do sometimes at weddings."

Verity patted her on the shoulder. "You're just getting a bit nervy," she told her. "All young brides are the same. They're always scared until they get inside the church and see the bridegroom waiting there, just as worried as they were. You'll be all right as soon as you see Harold standing there as solid as the Rock of Ages."

Supposing he weren't there, thought Gillian. The wedding would be off—there'd be nothing else to worry about. . . .

Quite unaware that her daughter's thoughts could be running on these unsuspected lines, Verity hustled her towards the stairs. "You must pull yourself together and get ready," she urged. "Do run along, or someone will come in and see you in that dreadful négligé."

Gillian began slowly to climb the stairs. "I wish I could shake off that feeling that something dreadful is going to happen," she murmured.

"Nonsense, child!" said Verity briskly. "Harold's a most dependable boy, and you're going to be very, very happy." She stood and watched Gillian disappear into her room, where Iris was waiting to help her to dress.

Verity sat down at her desk and went through her morning's mail. Presently she heard the door open, and Pleydell stood there, wearing striped trousers and a white shirt.

"Seen anything of Iris?" he asked.

"I expect she's helping Gillian to dress. Don't disturb them unless it's important. Is anything wrong?"

"It's this shirt—two buttons missing. I don't know why the laundry can't be more careful."

"You've got shares in the laundry," she reminded him. "Why not bring it up at the next general meeting?" She went and fetched her workbox from the window-seat. "I suppose I'll have to do it for you," she sighed. "Sit down while I thread a needle; unless you would prefer Iris. . . ."

"No, no; it's just that I thought you were busy."

"We're all busy. But you can't give your daughter away in a shirt without buttons." She sorted out a couple of buttons and found a reel of white cotton.

"I'd do it myself," he said, "but I can't thread needles very easily. I suppose I've been relying too much on Iris."

"She certainly has her uses," conceded Verity, prodding the needle through his shirt-front and impaling a button on it, "but I doubt if you'll always have her around. She made a dramatic entrance into our lives, and I've no doubt she'll make the same sort of exit.

"Yes, she was on the stage for a while," he informed her. "She told me all about it that night at Redsea. . . ."

"Was she in the first or the back row of the chorus?" demanded Verity, stabbing the needle viciously through the button.

"For all you know, she may have been quite talented," he ventured mildly.

"There would be no necessity for that while she had those legs and that figure."

"I know you're not very friendly towards her," said Pleydell. "But you have to remember that you brought this on yourself. If it weren't for you, we should never have met. The divorce was entirely your idea."

"She was well paid for what she did, and I can't for the life of me see why she should follow you here."

He shrugged. "You must admit she's behaved very well on the whole, and she's been a great help these past few weeks."

"She's tried quite shamelessly to get you to marry her," said Verity, snapping off the cotton and looking for the second button.

"I've had enough of marriage to last me for quite a while," retorted Pleydell, trying to sound indifferent.

"Then I wonder you allow your daughter to make the experiment," declared Verity acidly.

"Her life is her own," said Pleydell. "Harold is innocuous enough, and she'll get along with him as well as anyone."

Verity glanced at him out of the corner of her eye. His face was inscrutable. Of course, it was not surprising that he had become rather cynical about marriage, she told herself; not many middle-aged men could stand up to being jerked out of their domestic groove after more than twenty years, and a break of that sort was bound to have its repercussions.

"I try to take a practical view of Gillian's marriage," he went on. "I think she is going into it with her eyes open; that's if she has paid any attention to the advice I've given her."

Verity looked up quickly. "Advice? You mean you've told her to dominate Harold?"

He shook his head very deliberately. "Oh dear no. I've told her the exact opposite—to let him dominate her. I am convinced that's the only way a marriage can succeed."

She stopped sewing and sat back to look at him for a minute. "You don't think it's possible there might be some sort of fifty-fifty arrangement?" she suggested diffidently.

"It's too delicate a balance. One personality is bound to overwhelm the other, and it's better that it should be the man's. After all, that's nature."

"Oh," said Verity, knotting the cotton ready to sew on the second button. "You really think Gillian will give way to Harold in everything?"

"Almost everything. If she takes one simple precaution I put her up to."

"I'd be most interested to hear what that is," said Verity politely.

"It may not even be necessary. I feel sure Harold will consult her about all the important things."

"All the same, I'd like to know," persisted Verity.

Pleydell took a deep breath. "It's quite elementary, really. All she has to do is to make his mind up for him by little hints and chance remarks at exactly the right moment. Women soon get a flair for that sort of thing. It was when they didn't even bother to exercise that natural flair that marriages began to go wrong. When they refused man the pride of the illusion that he was master in his own home. Even when he was doing exactly as his wife wanted. I haven't realized it till lately, but a man gets a simply tremendous kick out of feeling that he is master under his own roof." He paused for a moment, then added, "That's why our marriage went on the rocks."

Verity sewed for several seconds in silence.

"I'm glad you told me," she said presently, though her tone was non-committal.

"It was my fault in a way for letting you get the upper hand."

"It's generous of you to admit that," murmured Verity, concentrating on the button.

"Yes, I should have taken the initiative at the start," he continued reflectively, "but you were too much of a handful. You had too much vitality. I was struggling for promotion at the office, studying for the Bankers' exams; it was easier to let you have your own way in domestic matters. One sees these things better from a distance; a sort of perspective in time."

"As long as you don't make the same mistake again," she said casually.

"No fear!" He seemed quite positive on that point. "You know you're a wonderful organizer, Verity, but I should have made you confine it to outside the home. You organized my private life until it was just a shadow of your own."

"You couldn't expect me to sit and twiddle my thumbs all day," she pointed out mildly. "I had always been used to doing the thinking for my father. He would hardly leave the house unless I made up his mind for him."

"Yes," he admitted, "I should have made more allowances for that, perhaps. When we were first married I had no conception of how active your brain would be. You were for ever planning something or other. If only you'd done it a little more subtly, and hadn't been so anxious for all the credit. If only you'd had the cunning to let me think one or two of your ideas were mine; just as I did with the chairman of the bank when he adopted my new sub-branch scheme. It's rather surprising that a woman with your brain didn't appreciate that, young as you were at the time. Look at it objectively, and you'll have to admit I'm right."

"I don't admit anything," she said quickly.

"Not even that our marriage was a failure?"

"We were simply divorced because it would save money." She snapped the cotton with an emphatic gesture, and stuck the needle into the reel of cotton, which she returned to the workbox. He fastened his shirt buttons, but made no move to go.

"You know quite well that money wasn't the only reason for our divorce," he insisted. "You were quite anxious to separate after all the success of your book."

"In that case, you've certainly had your revenge. I wouldn't like to be placed in the same humiliating position again that I've put up with lately."

He swung round and looked at her inquiringly. "What's all this leading up to?" he asked.

"To the suggestion that you might be in love with Iris."

He looked relieved. "But I told you I'm not in love with her. Didn't I beg you to stay here? I'm not the type who goes round making promiscuous attachments at my age."

She knew that his protest was genuine. He began pacing

up and down the room, his one shirt-sleeve flapping absurdly as he swung round.

"And there's no one else?" she persisted.

"Certainly not. You've seen enough of my life these last few weeks to know that."

She leaned back and surveyed him thoughtfully. "I wonder if you'll ever remarry, Andrew," she said.

He came to an abrupt halt and stood looking down at her. "If ever I do, the suggestion will have to come from me," he said. "You may depend on that."

"I can't see why that should matter so very much."

He regarded her with complete amazement. "I've been trying to tell you this last twenty minutes—and you agreed—that the suggestion should come from the man. It's absolutely vital; the difference between building on a foundation of rock or on sand. You'd see that at once if it were happening to two of the characters in a book you were writing."

"Nobody associates my books with real life," she reminded him.

"All the same, I should imagine you like your characters to be consistent with the laws of Nature."

"It's when they break the laws that they become interesting," she informed him. "And I'm quite capable of writing my books without any outside advice." Her voice took on the acid quality which had made him recoil in the old days, but something seemed to cross her mind, and she relaxed at once. "You'd better run along and dress, in case you find any more buttons missing," she urged in a more friendly tone.

He seemed about to continue the argument, hesitated, looked at the clock on the mantelpiece, then went off upstairs with a muttered word of thanks. Verity turned to her letters once more. There was only one that called for an immediate answer, and she had just begun it when Iris put her head round the door to ask if the flowers had arrived. Verity shook her head.

"Gillian's just got into her dress," said Iris. "It'll be a sensation."

"Not too much of a sensation, I hope," said Verity.

"If a girl isn't a sensation on her wedding day, she never will be."

"Maybe," smiled Verity, "but it must be the right kind of

sensation. Anyhow, it's very good of you to have helped her like this. I'm sure she's very grateful; in fact, we all are."

"It's been a pleasure," replied Iris, greatly mollified. "I'll do the same all over again for you two when you decide to get married."

"I don't think there is very much fear of that," replied Verity.

"Of course you will. I can always tell when people are planning to get married."

"Can you?"

"Yes, there's a sort of look in the woman's eyes."

"Indeed? What sort of look?"

"Oh, just a look."

"Nothing in the man's eyes?"

"That isn't important," Iris informed her.

Verity swung round in her chair and levelled a steady gaze at her. "And what sort of look would you say there was in my eyes?" she demanded challengingly.

"I can't describe it. I just call it the marrying look. It's been there ever since the night you arrived."

"It still takes two to make a marriage."

"It takes just one woman," said Iris, "and it depends on how determined she is."

Verity turned to her again. "I seem to have had the impression that you entertained a few designs of your own . . ." she murmured.

Iris shook her head rather wistfully. "I wasn't determined enough. I've always been too soft when it comes to the final issue."

"I can't say I've noticed it," retorted Verity, wishing Iris would let her get on with her letter. But Iris showed no sign of obliging. She perched on an arm of the settee and said in a confidential tone: "If you don't mind my mentioning it, that's your trouble. You don't notice things under your nose. You never appreciated half your husband's good points, or you wouldn't have wanted that divorce. Until I came here I never realized that writers could be so ignorant. They seem to get so wrapped up in their work they miss what's going on under their own roof."

"I'm surprised you don't write a book yourself," suggested Verity sarcastically, her nerves thoroughly on edge.

"I think perhaps I will when I get the time," nodded Iris thoughtfully.

"I've no doubt it will be an enormous success."

"I don't see how it can fail," said Iris confidently. "I shall put all my experiences into it."

"That should interest the censor. What will you call it?—'Revelations of a Professional Co-respondent'?"

"That's not a bad idea," said Iris, getting up from the settee. She seemed determined not to allow Verity's volley of innuendoes to pierce her armour of bland indifference. "I'd better see how the bride's getting on," she said, moving towards the door. Verity went on writing busily and made no reply. She still felt very uncertain of her ground where Iris was concerned. How long would she continue to impose on them after the wedding? Pleydell seemed to have no objection to her staying, as long as Verity was there too. Would he feel the same way if Iris went? Would he want to be left alone with her? She no longer felt sure even of Pleydell.

Resolutely, she dismissed the matter from her mind and concentrated on the letter, which she presently finished and thrust into her handbag. Then she went out and fetched the car, calling upstairs to Pleydell that she was off to the hotel to see if the presents were properly displayed.

Soon after she had gone a small green florist's van arrived with the bouquets. Erika took them into the lounge, and Gillian came rushing down to see them, negotiating the stairs with some difficulty in her long dress. As she reached the foot of the stairs the front-doorbell rang, and almost without thinking she stretched out a hand to open it.

A man stood there, with a flat brown-paper parcel tucked under his right arm.

"Nick!" cried Gillian.

"I've brought your present," said Nick. "Is it all right for me to come in?"

CHAPTER XIX

MAY THE BEST MAN LOSE

FOR two seconds they stood staring at each other. Gillian felt she was greeting a ghost; Nick thought he had never seen her looking so beautiful. Then she opened the door a little wider and said in a choked whisper, "Come in here——"

She led the way into the lounge, closing the door after them. He looked round the familiar room and tried to appear at ease, but was conscious only of the pale-faced young woman who seemed so anxious to avoid his eyes.

"Why did you invite me to the wedding?" he asked.

"I thought you might like to come," she replied, still speaking in a very low tone, "and I somehow wanted you to be there. . . . Don't ask me why."

He smiled at her. "We did seem to understand each other pretty well when I was here. I didn't realize quite how much until I left. In fact, I missed you a lot. . . ."

He seemed about to say more, but his voice trailed away. He took the parcel from under his arm. "Here's your present," he said.

She slowly removed the brown paper and protecting wrapper of corrugated cardboard. It was a picture of herself; the portrait he had started months ago. Clutching the narrow frame, she sank into a chair near the window. She could not take her eyes off the picture; it was like gazing into some strange dream mirror that revealed a series of secret selves whose existence she had suspected with a mixture of fear and wonderment.

"Gillian . . ." his voice broke in softly at last, "why are you looking at it like that? Is there something wrong?

She shook her head without speaking. Suddenly he saw her eyes were moist.

"Really, Gillian," he tried to rally her in a jocular tone. "It isn't as dreadful as that, I hope."

"It's—it's beautiful!" she gulped in a voice thick with tears.

"Yes, it is pretty good," he said lightly. "As a matter of

fact, I was offered a hundred guineas for it. But I told the fellow there had never been any intention of selling——" He broke off and said in a rather more anxious tone, "I say, it seems a bit of a nerve giving one's own pictures for a wedding present . . . but I thought as it was a portrait of the bride maybe people would overlook that."

She had recovered her voice now. "It's the nicest present I've had," she assured him. "But, Nick——"

"Well?"

"I'm afraid I can't go through with it."

"Can't go through with what?" he asked in a mystified tone, thinking she was trying to refuse the picture.

"The wedding," she said with another gulp.

He was plainly startled. "Gillian, what's wrong?"

"N-nothing. . . . I just can't go on with it."

He made a move towards the sideboard. "Stay there and I'll get you a drink," he said.

"No, I mustn't drink. The people at the church will know in a minute."

"If you're not going to the church, then it won't matter. Anyhow, I'll give you a peppermint to suck after." He poured two fingers of brandy into a glass and splashed soda on to it. He brought it across and she sipped it slowly. The colour which had drained from her face showed some signs of returning.

"That's more like it," he said, taking the picture which she was still clutching and putting it down at the side of the writing-desk. "Drink it all, and then you'll get a nice peppermint. You're looking wonderful . . . and everything's going to be fine."

She finished the drink and handed back the glass. "You must think me a dreadful idiot," she said quietly.

"Why should I? You've just had an attack of nerves, like an actress often gets on a first night. You'll be all right the moment the curtain's up."

"Everybody expects the bride to be radiantly happy on her wedding day," said Gillian ruefully.

"In your mother's books, maybe. But it doesn't always follow. It's only human to be a bit scared. You've nothing to worry about. You look quite perfect in that dress; they won't be able to take their eyes off you. You'll be a sensation."

"I don't want to be a sensation."

"Have another drink."

He went over and poured a smaller measure of brandy, which he brought back to her. "We all get these jitters on big occasions," he said. "You mustn't let it get you down."

"But I've never really faced up to it before; never seriously thought about what it can mean." She took a gulp of brandy.

He patted her shoulder reassuringly. "All it means is walking up the aisle of a church and saying 'I will' when somebody else says 'Wilt thou?' I tell you there's nothing to it."

"Oh, it isn't that part that worries me so much," she assured him. He watched her curiously as she drained her glass. "It's the idea of being married to Harold," she said slowly. "It somehow seems so—formidable. . . ."

Nick thrust his hands into his trouser pockets and paced up and down. "You've left this a bit late, haven't you?" he said at last.

"I—I've always felt that way," she stammered, and seemed about to burst into tears.

"Don't cry," he said quickly, "or you'll never get your eyes right in time. Fight it back, and we'll try and discuss this without getting emotional. We've got to think fast."

Gillian swallowed hard. The brandy was making her feel a trifle muzzy and she felt rather more relaxed after a while. She found herself wishing she could sit back in that chair for the rest of the day and chatter idly.

"What on earth possessed you to encourage Harold, if you're not in love with him?" demanded Nick in some perplexity.

"I didn't encourage him," she replied gravely.

He made an impatient gesture. "Really, Gillian, you can hardly expect me to believe that a girl goes as far as this without offering a man some encouragement."

"It was sort of out of spite," she said sullenly.

"Against a harmless type like Harold? You really expect me to believe that?"

"It wasn't against Harold."

"Then who, in heaven's name?"

"You," she replied simply.

He eyed her apprehensively, wondering if he had given her

too much brandy. "Would you mind telling me what I'd done to arouse your spite?" he said at last.

She shook her head obstinately. "I'm not going to explain any more."

"But it's quite absurd," he protested. "We've never had the slightest quarrel."

"I know."

"I have never born any sort of grudge against you."

"I should hope not."

"We have always talked things over in a perfectly amicable way, just as we're doing now."

"Yes, of course."

"In fact, we've almost been like brother and sister."

"Or uncle and niece, father and daughter!" she interrupted rather wildly, her voice breaking with suppressed emotion. "Do I have to make myself any clearer?"

She half-turned in her chair and buried her face against it.

"Gillian, darling," he murmured, leaning over her, "you don't mean you've let yourself in for all this on my account?"

She gave a little nod.

"But good lord, Gillian, I've never presumed—you know I haven't." Almost to himself, he added: "That's rather queer, come to think of it. I always have in the past."

"You mean with other girls?"

He nodded. "Lots of girls fall for the so-called glamour that surrounds an artist. I've never scrupled to take advantage of that before. I was always too inclined to be grateful for small mercies."

"You weren't very grateful for me. In fact, I think you must be completely allergic to me, as the psychiatrists say."

He looked at her for some moments without speaking. A tiny frown furrowed the ridges of his forehead just above the nose.

"I don't think it's that at all," he decided. "It may even be just the opposite. In fact, I'm just beginning to realize why I took such a time painting Verity's picture . . . why I've come to your wedding, though I hate them, and haven't been to one in years."

Gillian regarded him unbelievingly. "You're not seriously asking me to believe all that?" she demanded somewhat uncertainly.

He rubbed his forehead with his hand. "Wait a minute, Gillian. I'm not too sure of all this myself yet; though it becomes clearer every minute."

"I shall never even begin to understand men," sighed Gillian, her tears for the moment forgotten.

"Don't worry too much about that. The trouble will start when you understand them too well. We've got to come to a decision *now*; there isn't a minute to be lost."

He was sitting on the edge of a chair two feet away from her, leaning forward and looking anxiously direct into her eyes. "If you're really in love with me," he said in a tense voice, "will you run away with me?—Now?"

Gillian was completely taken aback. For a moment she doubted if he was serious, but he seemed to be awaiting her answer as if his life depended on it.

"But how do I know you love me?" she protested. "You've never even tried to kiss me."

"There's no time to go into all that now. We've got to work something out quickly. First of all, you must telephone Harold."

"You're crazy."

"It's the least you can do. You wouldn't have him go to the church with the best man and hang about like a fool while you are twenty or thirty miles away. . . ."

"But, Nick, I can't possibly——"

"We could go to a little place I know in North Wales, not far from Conway, and stay there until the fuss has died down. Then we could get married as soon as I can get a divorce. . . . It'll mean borrowing your family car I'm afraid, but I don't suppose they'll set the police on us."

"I'm not so sure."

"We'll leave a note to tell them everything will be all right, and not to worry," he decided briskly. "But first of all we must 'phone Harold."

He found the number in the telephone pad and quickly dialled it. There was an answer almost immediately, and placing a hand over the receiver, he held it out to Gillian. "Go on," he ordered. "You've got to tell him. It must come from you."

"I won't!" exclaimed Gillian in a loud whisper.

"It isn't fair to him if you don't," he urged. "Go on—take it."

Very unwillingly, she accepted the receiver. "Hello, Harold," she murmured tentatively. . . . "Yes, it's me . . . no, no, nothing wrong. . . . Do I? Well, I suppose I am a bit nervous . . . Are you all right?"

"Get on and tell him!" hissed Nick.

Apparently, Harold had overheard the interjection, without picking up the actual words.

"It must have been one of those funny noises the line makes," said Gillian hastily. "Yes, I'm all dressed, Harold. Practically ready. Are you? . . . Since what time? . . . Good heavens, you must feel like a tailor's dummy in a sunny window. . . ."

Nick was about to speak again, but she waved him impatiently aside. "Well, if you really want to know why I 'phoned," she went on, "it was about your buttonhole. I just wanted to make certain they'd arrived. . . . Is it all right? And Peter's? . . . That's good. All right, see you later, darling. 'Bye."

She slammed down the receiver and faced Nick with a defiant expression. "I'm going through with it," she announced.

"You're what?" he demanded incredulously.

"I'm going to marry Harold."

"But why on earth? . . . Ten minutes ago you were about to run away with me."

"I know. You shouldn't have tried to force my hand like that. . . ."

"But, Gillian . . . !"

"I hate masterful men," she snapped. "When you pushed me into a corner like that, it opened my eyes, I knew in a flash that we weren't really suited. I'd just been infatuated with you."

"That was pretty smart of you," he declared ironically.

"Wasn't it lucky I found it out in time?—lucky for both of us."

He took out his handkerchief and mopped his forehead. "I must say you've a pretty cool nerve," he told her, "and I hope Harold appreciates what's coming to him."

"Oh, he does," she replied confidently.

"But you still don't love him?"

"Not in the way you mean. But I'm very fond of him, and I'm going to marry him."

"You mean you'll feel safer with him."

She smiled faintly and nodded. She had recovered some of her assurance now. "You would find out right away if I didn't love you," she explained, "but Harold will never know."

"That's the neatest backhanded compliment I've had for quite a while," he told her.

"Try not to feel bitter," she advised. "Just think of it as a lucky escape."

"I'd be very obliged if you'd stop talking like Aunt Kate in the *Teenagers' Weekly*," he snapped, fumbling for a cigarette and lighting it. Gillian went over to the mirror and examined herself closely for any traces of tears.

"Does my make-up look all right?" she asked.

"Just like a Max Factor advert," he replied, with supreme indifference. He stood back a couple of paces and eyed her thoughtfully for a moment, in the impersonal manner of an artist preparing to begin his day's work.

"You must promise to let me paint you in that dress sometime," he said presently, having recovered his former composure.

Gillian smiled. "I wonder whether you really wanted to elope with me, or just to paint my picture."

"Both, of course," he said earnestly, wondering if she guessed the real truth. Women had a devilish sixth sense in these matters, he reflected; they could take a fiendish delight in extracting confessions of love, even when they knew in their hearts the man had nothing more than a passing interest. He regarded her anxiously as she pushed a strand of hair into place and smoothed the lipstick at one corner of her mouth. She seemed to be fairly normal again now; apparently the brandy had had a soothing effect without unduly upsetting her.

"If you care to wait, there'll be a car to take you to the church," she said in a coolly polite voice, as she walked across the room and picked up the picture.

"I must take this to go with the other presents," she said.

"I'd rather you didn't."

Her narrowly pencilled eyebrows arched in surprise. "Why-ever not?" she demanded. "It should be quite good publicity for you."

Before he could think of a retort there was a sound of

quick footsteps on the stairs and the door opened abruptly. Iris stood there in her new dark green dress, into which she had just changed.

"Gillian, you must come and let me fix your veil," she began. "It's getting terribly late and——" She caught sight of Nick, who had come forward at the sound of her voice. "Why, Nick!" she exclaimed. "What are you doing here?"

"Friend of the bride," he said in an attempt at a flippant tone.

"Do you two know each other?" demanded Gillian in some surprise.

"We used to know each other . . . in Chelsea," replied Iris somewhat hastily.

"In that case, you'll want to have a little chat about old times," said Gillian. "I'll call you when I'm ready for you to fix the veil, Iris."

She went out, closing the door firmly behind her. They heard her slowly mounting the stairs. When she had reached the top, Nick turned to Iris. "What the devil is the meaning of this?" he demanded. "What brings you here?"

"I'm living here for the time being."

"What as?"

"Friend of the family," she mimicked him.

The blood suffused his neck and mounted to his cheeks, and he was plainly in danger of losing his temper.

"This is another of your damned tricks, Iris," he snapped. "I tell you I won't stand for it."

Iris shook her head and sighed a trifle theatrically. "You irritate me so much when you talk like that, Nick," she said, "that I've a good mind to divorce you."

CHAPTER XX

HAPPILY EVER AFTER?

NICK slumped moodily into an armchair and glowered at her. "This is certainly my lucky day," he growled, feeling vaguely resentful that his wife should apparently be enjoying herself.

She caught sight of the portrait which Gillian had laid on the top of the desk.

"So that explains how you come to be here," she said. "How much are they paying you for it?"

"Nothing. It's a wedding present. I painted her mother in the first place."

"I've never seen the picture."

"It's on loan to a travelling exhibition."

She leaned against the mantelpiece and smiled at him. "You've been doing well for yourself since we split up, haven't you, Nick?"

"How did you know?"

"I heard rumours. And I read all about your picture of Lillian Forde after she won the Oscar. You certainly get around."

"I should imagine you don't do too badly yourself, or you'd have been pestering me for money before this."

"Did I ever ask you for money?" she demanded indignantly.

"As we were only together for a month, you didn't get very much chance."

"I could have got a separation allowance."

"It would have been difficult at that time. You were earning more money than I was."

She smiled. "Maybe I'll see what the magistrate says now you are a highly paid portrait painter," she mused.

"You won't do that," he replied confidently. "You were always far too independent. That was one of the main reasons we split up—remember? You had rather unorthodox ideas about keeping all your old boy friends after marriage."

"And you were as jealous as an old man who'd married a girl thirty years younger than himself."

"You gave me plenty of reason to be."

A smile twinkled round the corners of her mouth as she recalled some of the scenes between them. He thought she was much more attractive than when he had first known her. Though she had a new air of self-assurance, she retained all her old vivacity, which had been her great charm. He began to wonder how she had spent her life since she had flounced out of their Chelsea attic at ten o'clock one night over three years ago.

His speculations were cut short by Gillian rushing in, with her Juliet cap and misty tulle veil slightly awry.

"Do help me fix this, Iris," she pleaded. "The cars will be here at any minute now."

Iris's long fingers quickly made the necessary adjustments, while Gillian fidgeted rather impatiently and Nick gazed somewhat moodily out of the window. Finally, Iris stood back and carefully surveyed Gillian, from the dainty cap with its delicate network of pearls down to the tips of her silver slippers.

"When you take off the bolero it'll make a lovely evening gown for dances; that's if you want to go dancing after you're married," she commented, making another small adjustment. "For some reason, men seem to lose interest in dancing after they're married. At least, in taking their wives to dances."

"It's because most men shun any form of exhibitionism," suggested Nick.

"But I've noticed they're fast enough to take other girls," said Iris.

"That's merely a case of an inhibition being overcome by a stronger temptation."

Iris seemed inclined to argue, but there was a sound of cars stopping outside the front door.

"You two will be able to come together in the second car," decided Gillian. "There'll be heaps of room."

At that moment Pleydell came downstairs, carefully brushing the side of his top hat with his sleeve. This was the first time for over a year that he had worn formal dress, and he descended the stairs with all the dignity of an emperor making his final 'walkdown' in the palace scene of a pantomime. There was something about the cutaway morning coat, striped trousers and butterfly collar that give him a new confidence in himself.

This was the first time in twelve months that the Pleydell family had made a joint public appearance; all differences were to be forgotten and it was a day for rejoicing.

"Are you ladies ready?" he called from the foot of the stairs, and was slightly taken aback to find that they were. The car with Iris and Nick, which was to pick up the bridesmaids, left first, and Gillian and her father were to follow five minutes later.

When they had gone, Gillian looked quickly round the room, and at once noticed her portrait.

"Oh dear, they should have taken this with them," she said. "Perhaps we could leave it at the Feathers on the way to the church."

"I don't see why not," said Pleydell, studying the picture thoughtfully. "It's a first-rate piece of work," he said. "Young Nick knows his job. . . ."

He made the necessary arrangements with the driver, who was waiting outside, then turned to Gillian. "Well, if you're quite sure you've got everything, it's about time we made a move," he said.

Gillian picked up her bouquet and they went out to the car.

Despite her fears, everything went entirely to schedule at the church, where the ushers had meticulously assembled the bride's friends on the left and the groom's on the right. (She noted with satisfaction that the former seemed to outnumber the latter by four to one.) When the inevitable Wedding March struck up she was again slightly surprised to find herself in perfect synchronization with her father as they began their measured pace down the aisle.

Her eyes went at once to the far end of the aisle, to rest comfortingly upon Harold and the stalwart figure of his best man, Peter Staithes, the Firbright football star, whose enormous shoulders bulged so ruggedly that his coat seemed likely to split at the seams. And there at the altar was the venerable Canon Fosdick, looking as pleased as if he had arranged the match. The Canon revelled in what he called 'a traditional wedding', with all its splendour and frills. He always saw himself as the central figure, the supreme agent of heavenly benison. That no fewer than forty-eight couples on whom he had uttered a benediction had been separated by the divorce courts was apparently a matter of supreme indifference to him; it did not in the least affect the unctuous éclat with which he appeared to bestow the right to perpetual marital bliss.

The doughty Mr. Staithes produced the ring without any of that embarrassing fumbling which has been the comedy standby of film weddings since the days of the bioscope, and the Canon's address, though a thought too fatherly, was reasonably brief. Then Gillian found herself in the vestry, surrounded by what seemed like a horde of over-made-up middle-aged and elderly women, eager to congratulate her on getting her man.

Among the men there was a certain amount of sundry back-slapping; she signed her name in several blank spaces, received a copy of the certificate, and the organ began its Wagnerian peal as they made a rather less stately exit, with Gillian on Harold's left arm—so that his right arm could be free to defend from any dastardly attack by a disappointed suitor. It would be rather nice, too, if bridegrooms wore a sword, she thought, so that they could deal with such emergencies in a truly dramatic fashion. And most brides would revel in it.

She had hardly spoken a dozen words to her husband so far; indeed, there did not seem to be very much to say as they stood in front of the church and grouped themselves to the instructions of a brisk young photographer. The majority of the guests crowded into their cars and went on to the Feathers to await the arrival of the bridal party.

When they reached the hotel, Gillian and Harold found a large group clustered round a table at the far end of the reception room in which the presents were displayed. It seemed that the centre of attraction was Gillian's portrait, which was arousing a pronounced buzz of excitement.

Gillian was not particularly surprised, however, and concentrated upon being polite to the guests who surged past in the direction of the dining-room. She had to be introduced to dozens of Harold's distant relatives, whom he had never mentioned to her before.

"Keep the right side of the old girl," he muttered from the corner of his mouth as some newcomer arrived on the scene, and Gillian switched on a polite mask-like smile to greet a wizened spinster or gracious dowager, who was anxious to assure her that she had been blessed by the gods to secure such a man as Harold.

She moved slowly along the room, and by the time she reached the portrait the crowd had thinned out. Verity, who had been looking at the picture, turned to her and said, "Did you know about Nick and Iris?"

"I knew they'd met before. Why?"

Verity indicated a card tucked into the bottom corner of

the frame. On it a feminine hand had recently scribbled: *With love from Nick and Iris Arundel.*

.   .   .   .   .

In the speeches that followed, the convention that any schism between parents of the happy couple must be overlooked on their wedding day was studiously observed. Various speakers, who claimed to have known Gillian all her life, and Pleydell and Verity for the greater part of theirs, were lavish in their praise for them both jointly and separately. Inspired by the generous flow of the most expensive champagne obtainable, fine phrases floated around the room like balloons on a gala night.

Feeling extremely mellow, Pleydell replied to the toast of the bride's parents at rather greater length than he had originally intended. For once in a way Verity was not called upon to speak, and for some reason which she could not fathom was relieved at being spared what appeared to be an ordeal.

Everyone around seemed extraordinarily friendly, Pleydell reflected. And there were several so-called 'County folk' present whom he had hardly expected to see. No doubt the publicity Verity had been getting during the past year had attracted some of them. Still, the fact remained that they did not appear in the least stand-offish.

Several of the younger male element discreetly disappeared, bent on inserting a kipper into the exhaust pipe of Harold's car, and contriving various other booby traps to which honeymoon couples are so cruelly subjected. Meanwhile, their elders steadily pursued the more serious business of eating and drinking.

Verity went upstairs with Gillian to help her change into her travelling costume and pack the wedding dress.

Gillian was slightly flushed with the champagne and excitement of the occasion, and Verity thought she had never seen her looking so attractive. If she still harboured any qualms about marrying Harold, they seemed to be forgotten for the moment in the intoxication of finding herself the central figure amidst a hundred and fifty guests, with the spotlight following her as assiduously as if she were a prima ballerina.

"Isn't it fun about Nick and Iris?" she said, as she wriggled out of the dress and unfastened her suspenders preparatory to changing her stockings.

"Fun?" repeated Verity, with a slight lift of the eyebrows.

"Don't you think they're suited?"

"I haven't really thought about it. They obviously concluded they weren't."

"They never gave marriage a fair trial," maintained Gillian. "All Iris needs is a man she can be loyal to, and Nick wants a woman to look after him."

"Pity they didn't discover that earlier, if it's true," sniffed Verity dubiously.

"They were very young when they married; both of them have knocked about a lot since then."

"She hardly seems to me to be the right woman for Nick," decided Verity, carefully folding the wedding dress.

"You don't think she's the right woman for anyone," smiled Gillian. "But Iris isn't such a bad sort when you get to know her."

"She's very attractive sexually to most men; the type is quite familiar."

"Oh, stop dissecting her like a novelist," said Gillian. "She's human, and very good natured."

"They have travelled a long way in different directions since they first met," murmured Verity, who still felt vaguely resentful that Nick had never told her very much about his wife. She had always imagined herself as the type of woman who inspires confidences, and felt hurt when they had not been forthcoming.

"That means they are both probably more tolerant," persisted Gillian, as she fastened her skirt.

Verity shrugged. "Maybe. But I should have thought any man would have thought twice before marrying a woman who has been a professional co-respondent."

Gillian laughed. "It isn't as terrible as you think. Iris told me quite a bit about it. For instance, that night she spent with Daddy was a perfect scream; as innocent as a visit to the dentist."

"I'm sure that was no credit due to her," declared Verity acidly, as she swiftly ran a clothes brush over Gillian's travelling costume.

"Are the seams of my stockings straight?" asked Gillian, peering over her shoulder. Verity nodded.

Gillian sat down in front of the mirror and carefully renewed her make-up while Verity collected the rest of her clothes and packed them, ready to be taken over to the new house. She stared at Gillian, sitting there in front of the mirror, running a comb through her hair. She seemed almost like a stranger; Verity found it difficult to accept that her daughter was now a married woman, about to share her life with a young man whom Verity had known when he was a boy in knickerbockers attending the local grammar school. It seemed to Verity like the ending of an era, and gave her an uncomfortable feeling of uncertainty about the future.

For the past twenty years the future had seemed only too monotonously planned at times. True, she had always contrived to amuse herself, and Pleydell had been very tolerant, but there had been moments when she longed to break away. Indeed, once or twice she had succeeded in doing so. She had spent a week-end in Paris by herself, for instance, and she had toured the Lake District on her own, feeling more lonely every day, and eventually glad to get back to her own circle. There had always been Pleydell and home . . . though she had never fully appreciated them.

When it was time to go down she kissed Gillian good-bye quite impulsively, then remained in the background while most of the others joined in the hilarious farewells to the traditional accompaniment of showers of confetti, which bride and bridegroom would discover in all sorts of unexpected places for weeks to come.

After their departure there was the usual feeling of anticlimax, and Verity seized the opportunity to talk with her publisher, the ebullient Mr. Paskin, who took her into a corner of the lounge, where Pleydell noticed them drinking tea and talking seriously for nearly half an hour, at the end of which time most of the guests had left.

Paskin was as impeccably dressed as any man there, and, as usual, was combining business with pleasure. Already he had busied himself with the photographers, arranging for pictures of Verity and the happy couple to be sent to the London evening papers. He had arrived an hour before the wedding, and had spent the time chatting with the editors of two local papers, who also represented the London dailies. Mr. Paskin had not spent three years of the war in the Ministry of Information without learning something of the art of discovering the right contacts.

He refused an invitation to return home with Verity and announced that he must catch the next train back to town. After he had gone, and the remnants of the party were straggling towards the hotel entrance, Pleydell came over to Verity.

"I've settled with Hoskins," he told her. Hoskins was the landlord of the Feathers.

"Then we're almost ready to go. There are some of Gillian's things I want to take to the new house."

"What's happened to Iris?"

"I haven't seen her this last hour. Nor Nick either."

"They must have gone back to the house."

They found them waiting there, sitting in the lounge, with their suitcases out in the hallway. Iris was looking radiant and Nick quietly pleased with himself. Verity took command of the situation at once.

"I think we might all have a little drink," she announced, and Pleydell went over to the sideboard.

"We want to catch the seven-ten back to town," Iris informed them with a note of undisguised satisfaction in her voice.

Pleydell turned in the act of pouring a whisky. "Then I take it that you two have arranged matters to your mutual agreement?" He was still wearing his wedding outfit, and spoke in the somewhat pedantic manner typical of a bank manager. Nick could not repress a ghost of a smile.

"There's nothing signed and sealed as yet," he replied, "but we feel we should give each other a fair trial."

"That's splendid," said Verity, secretly relieved at the prospect of getting rid of Iris. "After all, there's nothing like marriage, when all's said and done."

Pleydell shot a quizzical glance in her direction, then returned to his decanter. When he passed round the glasses, sherry for the ladies and whisky for the men, they all stood as if expecting yet another toast.

"Here's hoping your second experiment will be more successful," Verity pronounced.

M

Iris held up her glass. "And here's wishing you the same," she responded sweetly.

Verity avoided Pleydell's gaze and took a gulp at her sherry.

"All the same," proceeded Pleydell in a slightly mystified tone, "I'm dashed if I can understand why you two kept your marriage so quiet; neither of you even mentioned the name of your partner."

"As far as I'm concerned, there never seemed much point," replied Nick. "And I dare say we were both slightly ashamed of our marriage breaking up after only a few weeks; we probably had some sort of psychological twist or repression. Verity would be able to explain it."

"I don't think there is any necessity to go into all that now," said Verity hastily. "The main thing is that you are determined to make a fresh start. You'll profit by your mistakes, I'm sure."

"I have a feeling that the solution to all our problems will be children," said Iris. "I've an absolute craving for them. Nick feels the same."

"Then that's simple enough," said Pleydell without thinking. "You just go ahead and—er . . ." He covered his confusion with a cough and took a pull at his whisky.

"Darling Andy; he's such a lamb," murmured Iris, exchanging a smile with her husband.

"That was a fine portrait of Gillian, Nick," said Pleydell, abruptly changing the subject. "Very decent of you to make her a present of it."

"Yes, I'm just the teeniest bit jealous," admitted Iris. "I'd no idea he'd been doing it."

"Never mind, darling," Nick consoled her. "I'll make a start on yours tomorrow."

"No, darling," said Iris. "On second thoughts, we'll have the baby first, then you can do one of those 'mother and child' things that always go so well at the Academy."

"That's a very bright idea," applauded Verity.

Erika came in to know how many there would be for dinner, and Verity asked Nick and Iris to stay, but they insisted on catching their train.

"Just the two of us, then, Erika," said Verity. "And we only need a very light meal——" She broke off as the thought struck her that she had not consulted Pleydell on this point, but he smiled and nodded when he noticed her hesitation. At the door as she went out, Erika paused.

"It was a most beautiful wedding," she observed wistfully. "Ever since, I have cried and cried . . . to think I might have had a wedding like that."

"Cheer up, Erika; you've plenty of time left yet," said Nick consolingly.

"To be married in white . . . it is so different . . . so beautiful," sighed Erika, blinking away a tear as she returned to the kitchen.

"We'd better get moving," said Nick, glancing at his wristwatch.

"Have another drink, then I'll drive you to the station," said Pleydell. "You've plenty of time."

"There's something about a wedding that's different," ruminated Nick as he sipped his whisky. "I think myself it's the pagan aspect that catches the imagination. After all, it's a very deep-rooted tribal ceremony. Why don't you make it a theme for a book?" he suggested to Verity.

"Why don't you use it for a picture?" she countered.

"Maybe I will," he laughed. "A mural."

They finished their drinks, and Verity and Iris bade each other such an effusive good-bye that a casual observer might have been forgiven for concluding they were twins about to be separated for the first time in their lives.

"Do come and see us as soon as you're back in Town," begged Iris, and Pleydell was astonished to hear Verity readily accept the invitation, as if there had never been a discordant word between them.

Verity stood on the front doorstep and waved them off, then went into the kitchen to help Erika with the evening meal. When Pleydell returned she said: "The *Firbright Messenger* editor was on the 'phone just now. He wanted to know what name I wished to go by—this is the first time they've mentioned me since the divorce was made absolute."

Pleydell frowned. "Yes, I suppose that is a problem," he said. "What did you tell him?"

"What did you want me to tell him?"

"Well, he could hardly refer to you as Miss So-and-so, the bride's mother."

"Just what he said. I told him it was quite legal for me to

go on using my married name, so I expect he'll do that. Anyhow, he's sending up the proofs the day after tomorrow, so that we can make sure all the names are there."

He nodded and sat in his armchair to put on his slippers. The house seemed suddenly deserted; he experienced a sense of anti-climax to the series of noisy and exciting events of the day. With some effort he refrained from taking another drink, telling himself that maybe some food would put him in a more agreeable frame of mind. He was fully aware that he had drunk far too much for one day already, and that possibly was the cause of his present slight depression.

"Well, it all went off much better than I expected," he said in a somewhat strained effort to relieve the silence.

"Not nearly as well as it would have done eighteen months ago—from the local viewpoint, of course," said Verity. "The Kirwells and the Maynards ignored the invitation. So did the Seymours and your Uncle Cookson."

"And your Cousin Penelope and Aunt Margery," he reminded her.

"They're Catholics; so they've a double excuse. They don't approve of divorce and they don't go in Protestant churches."

"Still, there were far too many people there anyway," he said, smothering a yawn. "I can't help feeling relieved that everything went off without a hitch."

"Why shouldn't it?" demanded Verity. "I'd planned it right down to the last detail."

"Yes, of course. But Gillian and I both had a sort of presentiment that something would go wrong."

"Girls always get these silly ideas."

He crossed his legs and eyed the toe of his slipper thoughtfully. "All the same," he murmured, "we've been in the public eye quite a bit, and I couldn't help wondering if there might not be an unpleasant scene of some sort; you never know what cranks are hanging around at these affairs. I remember going to a customer's funeral once, and a man jumped down in the grave and recited a long speech from *Hamlet*."

"He was probably an unemployed actor," said Verity.

Erika came in with the soup and broke off the argument.

"The house seems quite empty," she said presently, in another effort to make conversation. "Won't it be rather dull for you here?"

"I've got used to it. What about you?"

"It suits me," she replied. "Maybe I'll be able to get down to some real work."

"I don't see why not. I've a feeling you wrote that second book in rather a hurry. But won't you find this place rather quiet after Chelsea?"

"I don't really notice such things very much when I'm working. The fewer distractions the better."

"Of course, people will talk," he said presently.

"You mean about us living here together when we are divorced?"

He nodded.

"But we expected that, didn't we, when we made the plan?"

"Rather a lot of things that we didn't anticipate have happened since then."

Erika brought in two large omelettes and cleared the soup plates. When she had gone, Verity said, "You want me to clear out and go back to Chelsea?"

"I didn't say that," he replied cautiously.

"You hinted it pretty strongly. I don't mind, you know. I didn't really intend to stay as long as I have."

"It was good of you—saved me from rather an awkward predicament. But on this question of staying, I'm considering your reputation more than my own. People always blame the woman more than the man in these matters, and you have a name to consider. If any scandal gets round, it's bound to affect your sales."

"I doubt if mine is the sort of public that would be affected by that sort of thing," she mused, trying hard to fathom his mind. Did he really want to get rid of her? Why should he?

In some ways he had become an unknown quantity during the past year, a development which she found alarming at times, though it had a certain intriguing quality in some respects. For one thing, he was far more interesting to live with; he seemed to have developed a much more pronounced individuality.

"Suppose we consider the matter from your point of view," she surprised him by saying. "Now Gillian has gone, you'll be living alone with Erika, who is young and attractive. What do you think your friends at the golf club will say to that?"

He shrugged. "I suppose I can always engage a comfortable housekeeper with a face like a female warder," he replied. "But I leave it entirely in your hands."

"In that case," she said deliberately, "I'll go back first thing in the morning."

"You needn't rush away," he protested.

"There's not very much point in my staying on, is there?" she persisted. He wriggled uncomfortably on his chair and pushed his plate away from him.

"To tell you the truth, Verity," he began awkwardly, "I've been thinking quite a bit about us two, and I thought perhaps you might——"

He was cut short by the telephone bell, which seemed to vibrate right through the house. He went over to answer it, and was told to hold the line.

"It's a trunk call from Sandgates," he told Verity, slipping a hand over the receiver. "Must be Gillian; she's probably forgotten to pack something. . . ."

When Gillian came through, however, it was obviously something much more serious, as Verity could tell from his worried look as he listened in silence for about a minute. Then he began to plead with her, and Verity realized that there had been a quarrel of some sort.

"Let me talk to her," she said in a loud whisper, but he waved her away and went on arguing. Verity heard the three pips, but still the argument waged. She marvelled at his patience. He did not attempt to browbeat Gillian; all the time he was pleading with her, pointing out the disastrous consequences of doing anything rash, insisting on his confidence in Harold, telling her she had had a trying day and begging her to have a good night's sleep before making any big decision.

The pips had sounded again before he replaced the receiver, took out his handkerchief and mopped his forehead.

"Gillian's had a row with Harold and wants to come straight home," he said in a slightly hoarse voice. "I'm afraid you'll have to stay on a bit longer, if you don't mind."

"You mean she's coming back tonight?"

"No, I persuaded her to wait till the morning. She says she'll spend the night in a separate room."

"But what on earth have they quarrelled about?"

"As far as I can gather it began on the way down, when he

started telling her about an A.T.S. girl he was keen on during the war."

"Not exactly an ideal topic of conversation for a honeymoon," said Verity grimly. "I must say I'm surprised at Harold. I've always thought he never had eyes for anyone else."

"The war upset a lot of steady fellows like him," said Pleydell, looking more worried than ever. "She says she'll catch the first train back here in the morning."

"Rubbish!" snapped Verity.

"All the same, I think you'd better stay on a few days, dear, just in case of emergency."

He was surprised to see that she did not appear to resent the suggestion.

CHAPTER XXI

RIGHT ABOUT TURN

WHEN Gillian did not return the next day, Pleydell was uneasy, and would have telephoned her, but for Verity's firm opposition to the idea. She insisted that Gillian must solve her own marital problems right from the start, and that both parties would resent parental interference, however well-meaning. But Pleydell spent a restless day, with his ears always alert for the telephone or the sound of a car stopping in front of the house.

A certain restraint appeared now they were alone together, though Verity made an effort to retain her normal routine. There was, however, much less to be done now the wedding was over. In the afternoon she went out shopping, while Pleydell roamed around the house, then did a little work in the front garden. But there was no sign of Gillian.

By first post the next morning there was a picture postcard from Gillian. On the back was scribbled: *Lovely weather; have just had a wonderful drive through the New Forest. Gillian.*

Pleydell passed it to Verity across the breakfast table.

"What d'you make of that?" he inquired.

"I get an impression that they're on speaking terms again,"

she replied. "Give them time and they'll sort things out for themselves."

There were four more postcards during the next ten days, at the end of which time Pleydell felt rather more assured, though he was secretly surprised to observe that Verity never seemed in the least perturbed, even on the first day when Gillian had threatened to return.

When the third postcard, as non-committal as its predecessors, had arrived, Pleydell said: "I wish she'd tell us some news, instead of this nonsense about the weather and the scenery. Do you think we ought to get in touch with Harold's people?"

"I 'phoned them yesterday when you were out," Verity told him. "They've been getting exactly the same sort of postcards."

"You didn't say anything about Gillian's 'phone call?" he queried anxiously.

"Is it likely?"

"I suppose Harold hadn't 'phoned them?"

"If he has, they didn't mention it."

Pleydell shrugged and went on with his breakfast rather moodily. Since the wedding they had behaved to each other rather like a couple of guests who happen to find themselves at the same table at a seaside hotel. They were scrupulously polite at all times, and he noticed that Verity always consulted him before doing anything likely to affect the domestic routine. She spent a lot of her time writing, while he busied himself doing odd jobs in the house and garden. The weather was pleasant, and after all the rush before the wedding they were able to enjoy a certain amount of quiet and relaxation.

He was prepared to allow that Verity might understand the feelings of a young bride on her honeymoon better than he did, so he followed her advice and did not attempt to communicate with Gillian, who, after three days at Sandgates, had embarked on a short tour along the coast, so she was never at the same hotel for more than a single night.

On the day they were due to return, Verity sent Erika over to the new house to get it thoroughly aired for them, but she sternly vetoed Pleydell's somewhat wistful suggestion that they should go over and welcome the honeymoon couple.

When Gillian telephoned to ask them to tea the next day,

it was Verity who answered, engaging for five minutes in a completely non-committal conversation about hotels and scenery and people the young couple had met. Gillian made no mention of that telephone call on her wedding night, nor did Verity.

On their arrival at the new house Pleydell and Verity found the newly-weds standing affectionately arm-in-arm on the front porch, waiting to welcome them. As they conducted their visitors over the well-built and substantially furnished house, Gillian and Harold seemed almost entirely absorbed in and devoted to each other. Even so, they never overdid the endearments in the manner of some couples who put on a façade for the benefit of friends and acquaintances. Verity was on the alert to detect a false note, but discovered none. Pleydell was completely mystified, and often went minutes without speaking a word.

Gillian was quite obviously revelling in playing hostess in her own home, and both she and Harold chattered light-heartedly about their small holiday adventures and plans for the future. Pleydell sat balancing his saucer on his knee and putting in a cautious word from time to time as he tried to sum up the situation. He almost felt that the telephone call from Sandgates had been some form of strange nightmare, for Gillian had apparently quite forgotten it.

"Of course, this isn't our proper house-warming," she was saying gaily. "Harold and I thought we'd like you two to have a special private view first; there are lots of things we want your advice about. Then, when we've got everything really shipshape, we'll have a big party one Saturday."

After tea Harold took Verity down the garden to inspect a bed of begonias, on which he wanted her opinion, and they lingered on the way back to discuss the replanning of a rockery that needed some attention. Pleydell went into the kitchen and helped Gillian with the tea-things.

She managed to talk rapidly for nearly five minutes, but at last he had an opportunity to get in a word.

"Is everything all right now, Gillian?" he inquired with some hesitation. "Are you sure you're quite happy with Harold?"

Gillian regarded him with wide-eyed reproach. "Of course we're happy," she replied in a faintly injured tone. "Marriage is the most wonderful thing that ever happened. I'd like to see everybody in the world happily married; that would soon put a stop to wars."

Pleydell cleared his throat nervously in his embarrassment.

"I'm very glad to hear you talking like this," he said at last.

"But I'm only telling the truth," she protested.

He shook his head helplessly. "Well, if anything does go wrong, you can always come to me, and I'll straighten things out," he told her, feeling he owed that much to his conscience.

"Don't upset yourself about me," she told him. "It's you and Mother I'm worried about. Why don't you talk things over?"

"We've done nothing else for weeks."

"Marriage is such a wonderful thing," she repeated wistfully, "it gives you such a lovely settled feeling. You don't fret yourself about silly things like atomic bombs and secret weapons any more."

He carefully wiped a plate and placed it on top of a little pile. "You are talking to someone who tried marriage for over twenty years," he reminded her. "And perhaps I ought to warn you that there are times when that feeling of security isn't quite so—er—well, shall we say quite so cosy?"

"Oh well, all marriages are bound to have their ups and downs," she argued. "But you have to admit that there is something *basic* about it."

Pleydell could not restrain a faint smile. A fortnight after desperately announcing that she was going to leave her husband on her wedding night, here was his daughter delivering an impromptu lecture to her father on the subject of marriage.

"I hope you will always feel as positively as this about it," he murmured, stacking saucers and plates into a neat pile.

"Why shouldn't I?" she demanded challengingly.

"Well, you can't escape the fact that life is liable to all sorts of changes. I seem to remember that your mother and I were pretty enthusiastic at the start. . . ."

"And you're still in love with her," insisted Gillian.

"Well . . ."

"Of course you are. She's in love with you, too. Otherwise she wouldn't be here. She could have a far more hectic life in London amongst more congenial people, but she hates the idea of leaving you here alone."

"I don't think I'd put it as strongly as that," he began, a trifle dubiously.

"It was perfectly obvious to me when she came back from Chelsea. In fact, she's almost admitted it."

She was about to enlarge upon this information, but Verity and Harold came in from the garden at that moment, and the conversation at once became general.

Half an hour later, when Pleydell and Verity were driving home, he said: "They seem to be happy enough now. D'you think there was really anything in that business between Harold and the A.T.S. girl?"

"Does it matter?" said Verity rather absently.

"No, I don't suppose it does. Though I must say Gillian did seem quite upset about it when she telephoned that night."

"Brides are easily upset."

"Anyhow, she seems to have made a good recovery. She even gave me a lecture on the sanctity of marriage, with special reference to you and me."

"Oh, she did, did she?" Verity came out of her reverie with a jolt. "I hope you told her to mind her own business."

"Not in so many words," he grinned. "She really did seem genuinely anxious to see us together again."

She made no reply, and a minute later he carefully backed the car into the garage and switched off the headlights. He was just about to open his door when a thought struck him.

"By the way, I forgot to tell you I saw Wilkinson, the income tax inspector, up at the golf club this morning," he said. "I've a theory that he joined to snoop around the members—probably thinks anyone who plays golf must fall into the upper income group."

"Did you speak to him?"

"Oh yes, he managed to sidle me into a corner and shoot off a lot of questions about our present relationship."

"What did you tell him?"

"As little as possible."

Verity laughed softly. He took out a cigarette and lighted it at the dashboard.

"That fellow annoys me," he went on. "I appreciate loyalty to one's job, but after all there are limits. I gave him one or two fairly strong hints, and I've an idea he might have taken offence. Still, I was quite emphatic that we are to be assessed separately."

"I don't know that it'll make so very much difference next year," said Verity casually.

"What d'you mean?"

She took a letter from her handbag and switched on the roof light of the car. "This came by the mid-day post," she said, passing him the letter, which he opened.

It was from Paskin, and covered two closely typed pages. The style, as he expected from his brief acquaintance with the writer, was somewhat elaborate, and it was not altogether easy to find the core of the letter.

"This all sounds rather serious," he said at last.

Verity smiled. "It only means that the second novel is a complete flop," she replied. "That's why I won't be making nearly as much money."

"You don't seem very worried."

"Worrying's not much use, is it?" she said reasonably. "The book is written and printed and done with as far as I'm concerned. Personally, I think it's better than the first one. It just happens that the public doesn't agree with me."

"Poor old Paskin seems quite upset," murmured Pleydell, reading the last page again. "He writes rather like a head-master's end-of-term report saying this student must do better in future. This letter gives the impression that the firm will be out of pocket on the book."

"Maybe they will; but they made plenty on the other one. I'm not worried about Myles and Paskin."

"You don't even sound worried about Nina Nightingale."

"I can always write more novels if I want to. And if Myles and Paskin don't want them, there are several hundred more publishers. I'm tired of publicity and all that nonsense—maybe I'm getting too old to stand the constant strain of living in the public eye," she said thoughtfully. "Do I look much older lately?"

"You look exactly the same to me."

"Some days I feel a hundred years old."

"That's just the strain of writing the book. You'll soon get over it if you stay here quietly for a month or two."

She turned abruptly and faced him. "Only a month or two?" she asked.

He hesitated. "That all depends," he said at last. "I've tried to explain——"

"Depends on what?" she challenged.

"On your attitude to the idea of getting married again. If we try it, we've got to be completely frank with each other, or we'll be on the rocks once more. And I've no wish to become a laughing-stock, any more than you have. I've given the matter a lot of thought, Verity, and I've come to the conclusion that if we remarry, it will have to be a real marriage in every sense."

"I think perhaps you'd better explain that," she suggested gently, trying to conceal her sense of relief.

"First and foremost, I must have the right to plan my own life if I want to. You know I'm not the domineering type, but I must be master in my own house. If I can't have the last word in matters that affect the running of the house and my own home life, then there's no point in going on with the idea. In the past you have taken far too much for granted; presented me with too many *faits accomplis*. You've made all sorts of plans for me and invited people to the house without my knowing anything about it. I don't suppose I'd have disagreed hardly at all, but I've got to be consulted."

She was about to make a protest, but on quick second thoughts said nothing and waited for him to go on.

"I would never dream of asking anyone to stay, as you invited Nick, for instance, without mentioning it to you. It's only reasonable that you should do the same."

"Supposing you aren't available?" she queried mildly.

"Then don't issue the invitation."

Once more she bit back a retort.

"I'm quite prepared to do the same," he insisted. "And I'm not saying all this because I want to be overbearing. It's just that a home, like a ship, must have a captain."

"We got along for quite a number of years on the old arrangement," she reminded him.

"You might have been satisfied; I wasn't. Now I've got to take precautions to protect both of us. Twenty years' experience of marriage have convinced me that it's a much more highly complicated business than living in sin. This past year has been comparatively peaceful. I've done just as I liked when I felt like it."

"Then I'm surprised you even contemplate a change,"
Verity could not resist remarking, though she was careful to
use a pleasant tone of voice.

"I'm proposing it for several reasons," he informed her. "In
the first place, I am very fond of you, and I want to regularize
your position. It's the woman who comes in for far more spite
in affairs like this. I've heard it rumoured that you were in
the running for J.P. in the near future, and of course they
won't offer it to you unless your private life is beyond
reproach."

"Who says I'll accept?"

"You know it's the sort of thing you are best at; and you
enjoy it too. We've reached a time of life when irregularity
loses a lot of its charm, even if it's bearable in small doses.
That sort of thing is for the youngsters who are feeling their
way."

"Well, it looks as if I'll have to give up the Chelsea flat,"
sighed Verity. "It's lucky in a way that we've got Gillian off
our hands."

"Oh, I don't think we need worry too much about money,"
said Pleydell reassuringly. "You see, I'll be starting work
again soon."

Verity caught her breath in surprise, and waited for him to
explain. It struck her that it was rather queer sitting like this
in the garage, when they could have gone into the house, but
the car seats were very comfortable, and there was no chance
of their being overheard.

"Yes, I'm going back to the bank," he went on.

"But I thought they'd dismissed you."

"No fear! They couldn't do a thing like that simply because
I was divorced. What they had in mind was transferring me to
a subordinate position, but I had a private talk with the
sectional superintendent, and we came to an arrangement.
About that time, the bank was bringing in a new rule that
senior members of the staff could take a year's leave without
pay after twenty years' service if they wished to do so. It was
agreed that I should be allowed to exercise the option to give
the local gossip a fair chance to die down. Then they said they
would review the position. I'm pretty certain that they'll
reinstate me right away as soon as they hear we are getting
married again."

"Are we?"

"If you agree to my terms."

"And supposing I want to lay down a few conditions of my own?" she suggested.

"You have only to name them," he replied gravely. "You know I'm always ready to discuss things reasonably. But I think we'd better do it indoors; we've sat here quite long enough."

She reached over and squeezed his hand. "There aren't any conditions, Andrew," she said quietly. "This last year has taught me one thing at any rate—that it isn't possible to find a husband who suits me better than you do."

Andrew Brewster Pleydell was slightly surprised to find himself kissing his wife for the first time in five years and really enjoying it.

.   .   .   .   .

When they got inside the house they found it empty, which rather surprised them, for it was not Erika's night out. Verity went into the kitchen, while Pleydell wandered into the lounge and switched on the lights. He was scanning the evening paper when Verity came in carrying a single sheet of note-paper.

"It's just as well we decided to get married," she said. "Our last chaperone has gone."

"You mean Erika?" he asked.

"Yes, she's run away again."

"Good lord!" he exclaimed. "Who is it this time?"

"Tom Jackson, the gardener you engaged while I was away."

"Jackson?" he echoed incredulously. "But the man must be nearly sixty."

Verity consulted the letter. "Erika says here that he isn't really old; it seems he's been pursuing her ever since she got back."

"But it's ridiculous!" exclaimed Pleydell. "He's a married man with four children—one of them nearly nineteen."

"Don't worry," smiled Verity. "He'll go back to them." She folded the note and moved towards the kitchen door. "What would you like for supper?" she inquired.

Before he could reply, the telephone rang and she went to

answer it. After a brief conversation, she put her hand over the mouthpiece. "It's Gillian; she wants to know if we've made it up yet," she informed him. "Shall I tell her?"

"I suppose she ought to be the first to know," he agreed. She spoke into the receiver again. "It's all right, Gillian," she smiled. "The next time you row with Harold, you can come straight home to Mother."

There was a gurgle of surprise from the other end, and they broke into an animated but somewhat cryptical conversation as far as Pleydell was concerned. He went out to get his cigarette-case from his coat pocket, turning to lock and bolt the front door while he was out in the hall, just as he had done for a quarter of a century since the first night in their new home after the honeymoon. Tonight it seemed more symbolical than it had ever done before during the past ten years. He shot the bolts and turned the key slowly and methodically, then paused to light a cigarette.

When he returned to the lounge he sat on the settee and leaned back to enjoy his cigarette. Presently Verity replaced the receiver and came and sat next to him.

"What was Gillian saying?" he inquired.

"Gillian is still rather carried away by her discovery that marriage is the most wonderful thing in the world," she said. "And for once in a way, I agree with her. Now I really must go and see about a meal of some sort."

She was about to rise, but he put out a hand to restrain her. "There's no great hurry," he insisted. "We don't seem to have had a really cosy talk for ages."

Verity sat down again, leaned her head against his shoulder and gave a deep sigh of contentment.

"You're the boss," she murmured.

THE END